New Materials Reflecting the Tax Reform Act of 1986

The Tax Reform Act of 1986 has been described as the most significant change in United States tax laws since 1954 or perhaps even since 1913. Originally, we were afraid that this important new law would be passed too late for inclusion in this revision. However, we are pleased to report that the effects of the new law have been incorporated. This insert contains new study materials reflecting the textbook's up-to-date discussion of ACRS depreciation in Chapter 10. The new sections are printed in italics to emphasize the effects of changes in the law. These "A" pages should be used instead of pages 136, 137, 140, and 142.

Topical Outline (conclusion)

III. Accelerated depreciation for tax purposes

    A. Use of accelerated depreciation in preparing financial statements does not require that such methods also be used for tax purposes.

    B. *Depreciation of personal property*

        1. *Tax laws classify depreciable personal property into 3-year, 5-year, 7-year, 10-year, 15-year, and 20-year classes.*

        2. *Straight-line or ACRS accelerated depreciaton may be used.*

        3. *ACRS accelerated depreciation involves declining-balance depreciation with a switch to straight-line at the point where the switch further accelerates the depreciation.*

        4. *Since 1980, salvage values have been ignored.*

        5. *A half-year convention is assumed for the first year's depreciation.*

    C. *Depreciation of real property*

        1. *Residential rental property is classified in a 27½-year class. All other real estate is classified in a 31½-year class.*

        2. *Straight-line depreciation must be used, with a half-month convention for the first year's depreciation.*

        3. *Salvage values are ignored.*

IV. Control of plant assets

    A. Each plant asset should be separately identified.

    B. Periodic inventories should be taken to verify the existence and continued use of assets.

    C. Formal records of plant assets should be maintained.

        1. Controlling and subsidiary ledgers should be kept.

        2. Materiality principle may be applied for assets less than an established minimum cost.

Part I

Many of the important ideas and concepts discussed in Chapter 10 are reflected in the following list of key terms. Test your understanding of these terms by matching the appropriate definitions with the terms. Record the number identifying the most appropriate definition in the blank space next to each term.

_____ Accelerated cost recovery system (ACRS)

_____ Accelerated depreciation

_____ Book value

_____ Declining-balance depreciation

_____ Fixed asset

_____ Inadequacy

_____ Internal Revenue Code

_____ Land improvements

_____ Obsolescence

_____ Office Equipment Ledger

_____ Salvage value

_____ Service life

_____ Store Equipment Ledger

_____ Straight-line depreciation

_____ Sum-of-the-years'-digits depreciation

_____ Units-of-production depreciation

1. A plant asset.

2. The share of a plant asset's cost recovered at the end of its service life through a sale or as a trade-in allowance on a new asset.

3. A depreciation method that allocates depreciation on a plant asset based on the relation of the units of product produced by the asset during a given period to the total units the asset is expected to produce during its entire life.

4. The situation where because of new inventions and improvements, an old plant asset can no longer produce its product on a competitive basis.

5. Assets that improve or increase the value or usefulness of land but which have a limited useful life and are subject to depreciation.

6. A depreciation method in which up to twice the straight-line rate of depreciation, without considering salvage value, is applied to the remaining book value of a plant asset to arrive at the asset's annual depreciation charge.

7. A subsidiary ledger that contains a separate record for each item of office equipment owned.

8. A depreciation method that allocates an equal share of the total estimated amount a plant asset will be depreciated during its service life to each accounting period in that life.

9. The codification of the numerous tax laws passed by Congress.

10. *A unique, accelerated depreciation method prescribed in the tax law.*

11. A depreciation method that allocates depreciation to each year in a plant asset's life on a fractional basis. The denominator of the fractions used is the sum of the years' digits in the estimated service life of the asset, and the numerators are the years' digits in reverse order.

12. The carrying amount for an item in the accounting records. When applied to a plant asset, it is the cost of the asset minus its accumulated depreciation.

13. Any depreciation method resulting in greater amounts of depreciation expense in the early years of a plant asset's life and lesser amounts in later years.

14. The period of time a plant asset is used in the production and sale of other assets or services.

15. A subsidiary ledger that contains a separate record for each item of store equipment owned.

16. The situation where a plant asset does not produce enough product to meet current needs.

Part V

In January 1987, a company purchased an over-the-road tractor for $50,000. The tractor is expected to last 9 years and have a salvage value of $10,000. For tax purposes, the tractor is in the five-year class of assets, and the company is considering two depreciation alternatives: (a) straight-line over five years, or (b) ACRS depreciation. Complete the table by showing the amount of depreciation to be taken each year under each of the alternatives.

Year	Straight-line	ACRS Depreciation for Year	Undepreciated Cost at End of Year–ACRS
1987			
1988			
1989			
1990			
1991			
1992			

Part VI

A machine that cost $12,000 and upon which depreciation totaling $11,000 had been recorded was disposed of on January 1 of the current year. Give without explanation the general journal entries to record its disposal if the machine was sold for $1,000.

DATE	ACCOUNT TITLES AND EXPLANATION	P.R.	DEBIT	CREDIT

Part V

Year	Straight-line	ACRS Depreciation for Year	Undepreciated Cost at End of Year–ACRS
1987	$ 5,000	.20 × $50,000 = $10,000	$50,000 − $10,000 = $40,000
1988	10,000	.40 × 40,000 = 16,000	40,000 − 16,000 = 24,000
1989	10,000	.40 × 24,000 = 9,600	24,400 − 9,600 = 14,400
1990	10,000	.40 × 14,400 = 5,760	14,400 − 5,760 = 8,640
1991	10,000	($8,640/3) × 2 = 5,760	8,640 − 5,760 = 2,880
1992	5,000	($8,640/3) × 1 = 2,880	2,880 − 2,880 = −0−

Part VI

Jan. 1 Cash	1,000.00	
Accumulated Depreciation, Machinery	11,000.00	
Machinery		12,000.00

Workbook of Study Guides with Solutions I
Chapters 1-14

to accompany

Fundamental Accounting Principles
Eleventh Edition

Kermit D. Larson
The University of Texas at Austin

William W. Pyle

1987
IRWIN
Homewood, Illinois 60430

Printed in the United States of America.

ISBN 0-256-03581-4

1 2 3 4 5 6 7 8 9 0 VK 4 3 2 1 0 9 8 7

TO THE STUDENT

This booklet is designed to help you review the material covered in Chapters 1–14 of *Fundamental Accounting Principles*, 11th edition. You should understand that the booklet is not intended to substitute for your review of *Fundamental Accounting Principles*. Instead, the objectives of this booklet are as follows:

1. To remind you of important information that is explained in the text. For example, the topical outline of each chapter reminds you of important topics in the chapter. In reading the outline, you should ask yourself whether or not you understand sufficiently the listed topics. If not, you should return to the appropriate chapter in *Fundamental Accounting Principles* and read carefully the portions that explain the topics about which you are unclear.

2. To provide you with a quick means of testing your knowledge of the chapter. If you are unable to correctly answer the "Parts" that follow the chapter outline, you should again return to the appropriate chapter in *Fundamental Accounting Principles* and review the sections about which you are unclear.

Your best approach to the use of this booklet is as follows:

First, read the learning objectives and ask whether your understanding of the chapter seems adequate for you to accomplish the objectives.

Second, review the topical outline, taking time to think through (describing to yourself) the explanations that would be required to expand the outline. Return to *Fundamental Accounting Principles* to cover areas of weakness.

Third, answer the requirements of the Parts that follow the topical outline. Then check your answers against the solutions that are provided after the Parts.

Fourth, return to *Fundamental Accounting Principles* for further study of the portions of the chapter about which you made errors.

CONTENTS

1

Accounting, an Introduction to Its Concepts

Your objectives in studying this chapter should include learning how to:

Tell the function of accounting and the nature and purpose of the information it provides.

List the main fields of accounting and tell the kinds of work carried on in each field.

List the accounting concepts and principles introduced and tell the effect of each on accounting records and statements.

Describe the purpose of a balance sheet and of an income statement and tell the kinds of information presented in each.

Recognize and be able to indicate the effects of transactions on the elements of an accounting equation.

Prepare simple financial statements.

Tell in each case the extent of the responsibility of a business owner for the debts of a business organized as a single proprietorship, a partnership, or a corporation.

Define or explain the words and phrases listed in the chapter Glossary.

Topical Outline

I. Accounting as a profession

   A. Accounting is a service activity.
   B. All states license CPAs (certified public accountants).

II. The work of an accountant typically includes:

   A. Public accounting; the services of certified public accountants involve:

      1. Auditing—careful examination and review of a company's financial statements and accounting records to assure that the statements fairly reflect the company's financial position and operating results.
      2. Management advisory services—suggestions and advice for improvement of a company's accounting system and procedures.
      3. Tax services—preparation of tax returns, with advice as to how to incur the smallest tax.

   B. Private accounting; the work of accountants employed by a single enterprise involves:

      1. General accounting—the recording of transactions, processing of the recorded data, and preparation of financial and other reports.
      2. Cost accounting—the collecting, determining and controlling of costs.
      3. Budgeting—planning business activities before they occur.
      4. Internal auditing—continuing examination of the records and procedures of a business by its own internal audit staff.

   C. Governmental accounting; a variety of accounting positions in governmental agencies.

III. Important accounting statements include:

   A. The income statement, which indicates whether a business earned a net income (a profit) by showing the:

      1. Revenues earned—inflows of cash or other assets received in exchange for goods or services sold.
      2. Expenses incurred—goods or services consumed in the operation of the business.
      3. Net income (excess of revenues over expenses) or net loss (excess of expenses over revenues).

   B. The balance sheet—shows the financial position of a business on a specific date by listing the:

      1. Assets—property or economic resources owned by a business.
      2. Liabilities—debts owed by a business.
      3. Owner's equity—the interest of the owner (or owners) in the assets of the business.

IV. Generally accepted accounting principles—broad rules adopted by the accounting profession to serve as guides in measuring, recording, and reporting the financial activities of a business.

   A. Source of accounting principles

      1. American Institute of Certified Public Accounts (AICPA).
      2. Accounting Principles Board (APB)—established by the AICPA in 1959.
      3. Financial Accounting Standards Board (FASB)—replaced the APB in 1973.
      4. Securities and Exchange Commission (SEC)—the dominant authority in establishing accounting principles; relies heavily on the FASB.

   B. Important accounting principles and concepts

      1. Business entity concept—a business is separate and distinct from its owner (or owners) and from every other business.
      2. Cost principle—all goods and services purchased are recorded at cost.

3

3. Objectivity principle—amounts used in recording transactions must be based on objective evidence.
4. Continuing-concern concept—financial statements are prepared under the assumption that a business is a continuing or going concern.
5. Stable-dollar concept—the value of the dollar (the unit of measure used in accounting) is assumed to be stable and unchanging.
6. Realization principle—governs the recognition of revenue.

   Bases of revenue recognition:

   a. Sales basis
   b. Cash basis
   c. Percentage-of-completion basis

V. Business organizations include three general types:

A. Single proprietorship—an unincorporated business owned by one person.
B. Partnership—an unincorporated business owned by two or more people as partners.
C. Corporation—a business incorporated under the law, making it a separate legal entity distinct from its owners.

VI. Recording transactions

A. Accounting equation (or balance sheet equation)
   Assets = Liabilities + Owner's Equity
B. Double-entry system—every transaction recorded affects two or more items in the accounting equation so that the equation remains in balance.

Part I

Many of the important ideas and concepts discussed in Chapter 1 are reflected in the following list of key terms. Test your understanding of these terms by matching the appropriate definitions with the terms. Record the number identifying the most appropriate definition in the blank space next to each term.

4	Accounting	35	Equity
30	Accounting concept	23	Expense
44	Accounting equation	12	FASB
31	Accounting principle	50	General accounting
41	Account payable	20	Going-concern concept
27	Account receivable	7	Income statement
3	AICPA	16	Internal auditing
47	APB	37	Liability
42	Asset	34	Management advisory services
32	Audit	11	Net assets
1	Balance sheet	17	Net income
8	Balance sheet equation	21	Net loss
38	Bookkeeping	2	Objectivity principle
18	Budgeting	11/45	Owner's equity
43	Business entity concept	13	Partnership
29	Business transaction	14	Position statement
33	Capital stock	39	Price-level adjusted statements
40	Continuing-concern concept	28	Realization principle
26	Controller	15	Recognition principle
9	Corporation	6	Revenue
19	Cost accounting	24	Shareholder
10	Cost principle	46	Single proprietorship
48	CPA	25	Stable-dollar concept
36	Creditor	49	Stockholder
22	Debtor	5	Tax services

1. A financial report showing the assets, liabilities, and owner's equity of an enterprise on a specific date. Also called a position statement.

2. The accounting rule requiring that wherever possible the amounts used in recording transactions be based on objective evidence rather than on subjective judgments.

3. American Institute of Certified Public Accountants, the professional association of certified public accountants in the United States.

4. The art of recording, classifying, reporting and interpreting the financial data of an organization.

5. The phase of public accounting dealing with the preparation of tax returns and with advice as to how transactions may be completed in a way as to incur the smallest tax liability.

6. An inflow of assets, not necessarily cash, in exchange for goods and services sold.

7. A financial statement showing revenues earned by a business, the expenses incurred in earning the revenues, and the resulting net income or net loss.

8. Another name for the accounting equation.

9. A business incorporated under the laws of a state or other jurisdiction.

10. The accounting rule that requires assets and services plus any resulting liabilities to be taken into the accounting records at cost.

11. Assets minus liabilities.

12. Financial Accounting Standards Board, the seven-member board that currently has the authority to formulate and issue pronouncements of generally accepted accounting principles.

13. An association of two or more persons to co-own and operate a business for profit.

14. Another name for the balance sheet.

15. Another name for the realization principle.

16. A continuing examination of the records and procedures of a business by its own internal audit staff to determine if established procedures and management directives are being followed.

17. The excess of revenues over expenses.

18. The phase of accounting dealing with planning the activities of an enterprise and comparing its actual accomplishments with the plan.

19. The phase of accounting that deals with collecting and controlling the costs of producing a given product or service.

20. Another name for the continuing-concern concept.

21. The excess of expenses over revenues.

22. A person or enterprise that owes a debt.

23. Goods or services consumed in operating an enterprise.

24. A person or enterprise owning a share or shares of stock in a corporation. Also called a stockholder.

25. The idea that the purchasing power of the unit of measure used in accounting, the dollar, does not change.

26. The chief accounting officer of a large business.

27. An amount receivable from a debtor for goods or services sold on credit.

28. The accounting rule that defines a revenue as an inflow of assets, not necessarily cash, in exchange for goods or services and requires the revenue to be recognized at the time, but not before, it is earned.

29. An exchange of goods, services, money, and/or the right to collect money.

30. An abstract idea that serves as a basis in the interpretation of accounting information.

31. A broad rule adopted by the accounting profession as a guide in measuring, recording, and reporting the financial affairs and activities of a business.

32. A critical exploratory review by a public accountant of the business methods and accounting records of an enterprise, made to enable the accountant to express an opinion as to whether the financial statements of the enterprise fairly reflect its financial position and operating results.

33. Ownership equity in a corporation resulting from the sale of shares of the corporation's stock to its stockholders.

34. The phase of public accounting dealing with the design, installation, and improvement of a client's accounting system, plus advice on planning, budgeting, forecasting, and all other phases of accounting.

35. A right, claim, or interest in property.

36. A person or enterprise to whom a debt is owed.

37. A debt owed.

38. The record-making phase of accounting.

39. Financial statements showing amounts adjusted for changes in the purchasing power of money.

40. The idea that a business is a going concern that will continue to operate, using its assets to carry on its operations and, with the exception of merchandise, not offering the assets for sale.

41. A debt owed to a creditor for goods or services purchased on credit.

42. A property or economic resource owned by an individual or enterprise.

43. The idea that a business is separate and distinct from its owner or owners and from every other business.

44. An expression in dollar amounts of the equivalency of the assets and equities of an enterprise, usually stated Assets = Liabilities + Owner's Equity. Also called the balance sheet equation.

45. The equity of the owner (owners) of a business in the assets of the business.

46. A business owned by one individual.

47. Accounting Principles Board, a committee of the AICPA that was responsible for formulating accounting principles.

48. Certified public accountant, an accountant who has met legal requirements as to age, education, experience, residence, and moral character and is licensed to practice public accounting.

49. Another name for a shareholder.

50. That phase of accounting dealing primarily with recording transactions, processing the recorded data, and preparing financial statements.

Part II

Complete the following by filling in the blanks.

1. The _____ Cost _____ principle of accounting requires that all goods and services be recorded at cost. Goods and services are recorded at cost because normally

   costs are objectively established and thus meet the requirements of the _____

   _____ objectivity _____ principle, the accounting principle which requires that transaction amounts be objectively established. It is important that transaction amounts be objectively established because if accounting information is to be fully useful, it must be

   based on _____ objective _____ data and information.

2. The _____ Corporation _____ is a form of business organization that requires the organizers to obtain a charter from one of the states or the federal government.

7

3. Under the _____ *business entity* _____ concept, for accounting purposes, every business is conceived to be a separate entity, separate and distinct from its _____ *owner(s)* _____ or _____ *shareholders* _____ and from every other _____ *business* _____.

4. Does a balance sheet show current market values for the assets listed on it? _*No*_ (Yes or No) If the dollar amounts do not represent current market values, what do they represent? _*Costs at times of transactions. /w/ depreciation.*_ _____ _____.

5. Recognition of revenue when a sale or service has been completed is known as the _____ *Sales* _____ basis of revenue recognition.

6. Owner's equity in business is the _____ *interest* _____ of the owner in the net assets of the business.

7. The balance sheet equation is _____ *Assets* _____ equal _____ *Liabilities* _____ plus _____ *Owners Equity* _____. It is also called the _____ *Acctng* _____ equation.

8. The liabilities of a business are its _____ *debts* _____.

9. Accounting is a service activity, the function of which is _*to provide economic info, primarily financial in nature.*_ _____.

10. The assets of a business are the _*properties & economic resources*_ _____ owned by the business.

11. Bookkeeping is the _____ *record* _____-making part of accounting, and book-keeping and accounting _____ (are, (are not)) the same thing.

12. There are several kinds of accounting work done by employees of business firms. These include (a) _*general acctng*_, (b) _*cost acctng*_ _____, (c) _*budgeting*_, and (d) _*internal auditing*_.

13. An income statement prepared for a business shows whether or not the business earned a _____ *net income* _____ or suffered a _____ *net loss* _____.

14. A balance sheet prepared for a business shows its financial position on specific _____ *dates* _____. Financial position is shown by listing the _____ *assets* _____ of the business, its _____ *liabilities* _____, and the _____ *owners equity* _____ of the owner or owners in the business.

8

15. Expenses are goods and services _____consumed_____ in operating a business or other economic unit.

16. Revenues are inflows of _____cash_____ or other _____assets_____ received in exchange for goods or services provided customers.

17. The accounting equation for a single proprietorship is _____Assets = Liabilities + Owners Equity._____ _____.

Part III

The assets, liabilities, and owner's equity of Susan Thompson in a law practice are shown on the first line in the equation; and following the equation are eight transactions completed by Ms. Thompson. Show by additions and subtractions in the spaces provided the effects of each transaction on the items of the equation. Show new totals after each transaction as in Illustration 1-7 in your text.

	Cash	+ Accounts Receivable	+ Prepaid Rent	+ Law Library	+ Office Equipment =	Accounts Payable	+ S. T. Thompson, Capital
	$4,000			$8,000	$7,250		$19,250
1.	-3000		+3000				
	1000		3000	8000	7,250		19250
2.	-900				900		
	100		3000	8000	8150		19250
3.	+2500						2500
	2600						21750
4.	-700			+700		700	
	-700			8700			
5.		-1500					1500
		-1500					23,250
6.	-700					-700	
	1900					0	
7.	1500	+1500					
	3400	0					
8.	575						-575
	2825						22675

1. Paid the rent for three months in advance on the law office, $3,000.
2. Purchased a new typewriter for the office, paying cash, $900.
3. Completed legal work for Ray Holland, a client, and immediately collected $2,500 in cash in full payment therefor.
4. Purchased on credit from Legal Book Publishers law books costing $700.
5. Completed on credit $1,500 of legal work for Julie Landon and immediately entered in the accounting records both the right to collect and the revenue earned.
6. Paid Legal Book Publishers for the books purchased in Transaction 4.
7. Received $1,500 from Julie Landon for the legal work of Transaction 5.
8. Paid the weekly salary of the office secretary, $575.

Refer to your completed work on the previous page and fill in the blanks.

a. Did each transaction affect two items of the equation? _____. (Yes or No)

b. Did the equation remain in balance after the effect or effects of each transaction were entered? _____. (Yes or No)

c. If the equation did not remain in balance after the effect or effects of each transaction were entered, this indicated that _____error made_____
_____.

d. Ms. Thompson earned $2,500 of revenue upon the completion of Transaction 3 and the asset that flowed into her practice as a result of this transaction was in the form of _____
_____Cash_____.

e. Ms. Thompson earned $1,500 of revenue upon the completion of Transaction 5, and the asset that flowed into the law practice upon the completion of this transaction was ___
_____right to collect 1500_____
_____.

f. The right to collect $1,500 from Julie Landon was converted into ___cash_____
_____ in Transaction 7. Nevertheless, although the $1,500 was not received in cash until Transaction 7, the revenue was earned upon the completion of the _____work_____ in Transaction 5.

g. The $1,500 collected in Transaction 7 was recognized as revenue in Transaction 5 because of the requirements of the _____realization_____ principle, which (1) defines a revenue as an inflow of assets, not necessarily _____Cash_____
_____ in exchange for goods or services;
(2) requires that the revenue be recognized at the time, but not before, it is _____
_____earned_____, which generally is at the time title to goods sold is
_____completed (transferred)___ or services are _____rendered_____; and (3) requires that the amount of revenue recognized be measured by the cash received plus the cash equivalent of any other _____asset_____ received.

10

Solutions for Chapter 1

Part I

Part II

1. cost, objectivity, objective

2. corporation

3. business entity, owner, owners, business

4. No. Costs or costs less accumulated depreciation. (The phrase "accumulated depreciation" will be explained further in Chapter 3.)

5. sales

6. interest or ownership right

7. Assets, Liabilities, Owner's Equity, accounting

8. debts

9. to provide information, primarily financial in nature, about economic entities

10. properties or economic resources

11. record, are not

12. (a) general accounting
    (b) cost accounting
    (c) budgeting
    (d) internal auditing

13. net income, net loss

14. date, assets, liabilities, equity

15. consumed

16. cash, assets (properties)

17. Assets = Liabilities + Owner's Equity

    or

    Assets − Liabilities = Owner's Equity

Part III

	Cash	+	Accounts Receivable	+	Prepaid Rent	+	Law Library	+	Office Equipment	=	Accounts Payable	+	Susan Thompson Capital
	$4,000						$8,000		$7,250				$19,250
1.	−3,000				+3,000								
	$1,000				$3,000		$8,000		$7,250				$19,250
2.	− 900								+ 900				
	$ 100				$3,000		$8,000		$8,150				$19,250
3.	+2,500												+ 2,500
	$2,600				$3,000		$8,000		$8,150				$21,750
4.							+ 700				+ 700		
	$2,600				$3,000		$8,700		$8,150		$ 700		$21,750
5.			+1,500										+ 1,500
	$2,600		$1,500		$3,000		$8,700		$8,150		$ 700		$23,250
6.	− 700										− 700		
	$1,900		$1,500		$3,000		$8,700		$8,150		$ 0		$23,250
7.	+1,500		−1,500										
	$3,400		$ 0		$3,000		$8,700		$8,150		$ 0		$23,250
8.	− 575												− 575
	$2,825		$ 0		$3,000		$8,700		$8,150		$ 0		$22,675

a. Yes

b. Yes

c. an error had been made

d. cash

e. the right to collect $1,500 from Julie Landon, an account receivable

f. cash, legal work

g. realization (or recognition), cash, earned, transferred, rendered, asset or assets

2

Recording Transactions

Your objectives in studying this chapter should include learning how to:

Explain the mechanics of double-entry accounting and tell why transactions are recorded with equal debits and credits.

State the rules of debit and credit and apply the rules in recording transactions.

Tell the normal balance of any asset, liability, or owner's equity account.

Record transaction in a General Journal, post to the ledger accounts, and prepare a trial balance to test the accuracy of the recording and posting.

Define or explain the words and phrases listed in the chapter Glossary.

Topical Outline

I. Steps in the accounting process include:

    A. Identifying transactions—determining in what way business transactions affect a company.

    B. Recording transactions—translating transactions into accounting terms and entering transactions into the accounting system.

    C. Summarizing the effects of business transactions by preparing periodic reports, such as the balance sheet and income statement.

II. Accounting records include:

    A. Business papers—original source documents (invoices, sales slips, etc.) that provide information used in making accounting entries.

    B. Journal—book of original entry in which transactions are first recorded.

    C. Ledger—book containing a group of accounts in which information is posted from a journal.

III. Accounts are locations in the accounting system in which are summarized the increases, decreases, and balance of each asset, liability, owner's equity, revenue, and expense item.

    A. Types of accounts include:

        1. Asset accounts (Cash, Accounts Receivable, Supplies, Buildings, Land, etc.)

        2. Liability accounts (Accounts Payable, Notes Payable, Unearned Revenue, etc.)

        3. Owner's equity accounts (Capital account, Withdrawals account, Revenue and Expense accounts)

    B. Accounts are either *real* (balance sheet accounts) or *nominal* (income statement accounts).

    C. T-account—an abbreviated account form used as an aid in recording transactions by separating increases and decreases.

    D. Balance-column account (standard account form)—an account having a column for entering the new account balance after each debit or credit is posted.

IV. The mechanics of double-entry accounting—Assets = Liabilities + Owner's Equity

    A. Debit—the left-hand side of a T-account.

    B. Credit—the right-hand side of a T-account.

    C. Asset accounts are debited for increases and credited for decreases.

    D. Liability and owner equity accounts are debited for decreases and credited for increases.

V. Journalizing—the process of recording transactions in the journal which makes it possible to trace debits and credits into the accounts and to see that they are properly recorded.

VI. Posting—the process of copying information from the journal to the ledger.

VII. Trial balance—a list of accounts having balances in the ledger, the debit or credit balance of each account, and the total balances.

VIII. Bookkeeping techniques

    A. Locating and correcting errors by checking journalizing and posting procedures.

    B. Omission of commas, decimal points, dollar signs and zeros (in the cents column) of accounts and ledgers.

Part I

Many of the important ideas and concepts discussed in Chapter 2 are reflected in the following list of key terms. Test your understanding of these terms by matching the appropriate definitions with the terms. Record the number identifying the most appropriate definition in the blank space next to each term.

16	Account	18	Journal
30	Account balance	8	Journal page number
6	Account number	23	Ledger
3	Balance column account	1	Mortgage payable
20	Book of final entry	28	Nominal accounts
19	Book of original entry	4	Normal balance of an account
29	Business paper	13	Personal account
10	Capital account	24	Posting
17	Compound journal entry	27	Posting reference (P.R.) column
21	Credit	12	Posting reference numbers
11	Debit	22	Promissory note
26	Double-entry accounting	25	Real accounts
9	Drawing account	7	T-account
15	Folio column	2	Trial balance
5	General journal	14	Withdrawals account

1. A debt, usually long term, that is secured by a special claim against one or more assets of the debtor.

2. A list of accounts having balances in the ledger, the debit or credit balance of each account, the total of the debit balances, and the total of the credit balances.

3. An account having a column for entering the new account balance after each debit or credit is posted to the account.

4. The usual kind of balance, either debit or credit, that a given account has and that is a debit balance if increases are recorded in the account as debits and a credit balance if increases are recorded as credits.

5. A book of original entry in which any type of transaction can be recorded.

6. An identifying number assigned to an account.

7. An abbreviated account form, two or more of which are used in illustrating the debits and credits required in recording a transaction.

8. A posting reference number entered in the Posting Reference column of each account to which an amount is posted and which shows the page of the journal from which the amount was posted.

9. Another name for the withdrawals account.

10. An account used to record the more or less permanent changes in the equity of an owner in his or her business.

11. The left-hand side of a T-account.

16

12. Journal page numbers and ledger account numbers used as a cross-reference between amounts entered in a journal and posted to the ledger accounts.

13. Another name for the withdrawals account.

14. The account used to record the withdrawals from a business by its owner of cash or other assets intended for personal use. Also known as personal account or drawing account.

15. Another name for the Posting Reference column.

16. An accounting device used in recording and summarizing the increases and decreases in a revenue, an expense, asset, liability, or owner's equity item.

17. A journal entry having more than one debit or more than one credit.

18. A book of original entry in which transactions are first recorded and from which transaction amounts are posted to the ledger accounts.

19. A journal in which transactions are first recorded.

20. A ledger to which amounts are posted.

21. The right-hand of a T-account.

22. An unconditional written promise to pay a definite sum of money on demand or at a fixed or determinable future date.

23. A group of accounts used by a business in recording its transactions.

24. Transcribing the debit and credit amounts from a journal to the ledger accounts.

25. The balance sheet accounts.

26. An accounting system in which each transaction affects and is recorded in two or more accounts with equal debits and credits.

27. A column in a journal and in each account for entering posting reference numbers. Also called a folio column.

28. The income statement accounts.

29. A sales ticket, invoice, check, or other document arising in and providing evidence of the completion of a transaction.

30. The difference between the increases and decreases recorded in an account.

Part II

Complete the following by filling in the blanks.

1. A group of accounts used by a business in recording its transactions is called _____ *a ledger* .

2. If transactions are recorded by entering debits and credits directly in the accounts, errors are difficult to locate because even with a transaction having only one debit and one credit, the debit is entered on one page of the ledger and the credit on another, and there is nothing to _____ *link* _____ the debit and credit together. For this reason transactions are first recorded in a _____ *journal* _____ and are then posted to the ledger accounts.

3. The balance of an account is _____ *difference in debits & credits* _____ .

4. A journal entry linking together the debits and credits of a transaction makes it possible to _____ *trace debits & credits* _____ into the accounts and to see that they are equal and were properly recorded.

5. A T-account has a left side and a right side; and in entering increases and decreases in a T-account, the _____ *debits* _____ are placed on one side of the account and the _____ *credits* _____ are placed on the other side. This placement makes it possible to add the increases, add the decreases, and subtract the sum of the decreases from the sum of the increases to learn the amount of the item recorded in the account that the business has, owns, or owes.

6. The last step in posting an amount is _____ *entering the ref # in folio column* _____ . Making this the last step enables the bookkeeper to scan the _____ *Folio Column* _____ in the journal to see where posting stopped.

7. Accounts are a device used by a business in recording and summarizing the _____ *increases* _____ and _____ *decreases* _____ in each asset, liability, and owner equity item appearing on its balance sheet and each revenue and expense on its income statement.

8. The steps in preparing a trial balance are: _____
   1. balance each acct
   2. list aclts in ledger order w/ debits & credits
   3. sum debit
   4. sum credits
   5. compare totals for equality

18

_____

_____

_____

_____

9. Revenues increase owner equity and are ___Credited___ to revenue accounts. Expenses decrease owner equity and are ___debited___ to expense accounts.

10. a. The normal balance of an asset account, such as Cash is ___~~credit~~ debit___.
    b. The normal balance of a contra asset account is ___~~debit~~ credit___.
    c. The normal balance of a liability account is ___~~debit~~ credit___.
    d. The normal balance of the owner's Capital account is ___Credit___.
    e. The normal balance of the owner's Withdrawals account is ___debit___.
    f. The normal balance of a revenue account is ___credit___.
    g. The normal balance of an expense account is ___debit___.

11. Increases in assets are recorded as _____ ((debits), credits) and decreases are recorded as ___Credits___. Likewise, increases in liability and owner equity items are recorded as ___credits___ and decreases are recorded as ___debits___.

12. When an account has an opposite from normal kind of balance, this opposite from normal kind of balance is indicated by ___red ink or circle___

_____

_____

_____

13. Debits to accounts _____ (are, (are not)) always increases.

14. A trial balance that fails to balance is proof that ___error___ _____ either in recording transactions, posting, or in preparing the trial balance.

15. An account will normally have a _____ ((debit), credit) balance if increases are entered in the account as debits. Likewise, the normal balance of an account will be a ___cr___ balance if increases are entered as credits.

16. A trial balance that balances is not absolute proof that there were no errors in recording, posting, and preparing the trial balance because ___errors not affecting___ ___balance may been made.___

_____

_____

17. In a double-entry accounting system, transactions are recorded with equal debits and credits so that the equality of the debits and credits may be used as a test of _recording accuracy_.

18. The left side of a T-account is called the _dr_ side and the right side is called the _cr_ side. To enter an amount on the left side of a T-account is to _dr_ the account and to enter an amount on the right side is to _cr_ the account.

19. In a balance-column account the Debit and Credit columns are placed side by side and a third or _balance_ column is added. When such an account is used, its new balance is determined and entered in the _balance_ column each time the account is debited or credited; and as a result, the last amount in the Balance column is the _acct's current balance_.

Part III

Jon Wheeler has just begun a new small repairs business he calls Jon's Repair Shop, and the first ten transactions completed by the business follow:

a. Mr. Wheeler sold a personal investment in Southern Cable stock for $1,921.50 and began his business by depositing $1,800 of the proceeds in a bank account opened in the name of the business.
b. Paid three months' rent in advance on the shop space, $675.
c. Purchased repair equipment for cash, $700.
d. Completed repair work for customers and collected cash therefor, $505.50.
e. Purchased additional repair equipment on credit from Comet Company, $415.50.
f. Completed repair work on credit for Fred Baca, $175.
g. Paid Comet Company $290.50 of the amount owed to it.
h. Paid the local radio station $75.00 for an announcement of the shop opening.
i. Fred Baca paid for the work of Transaction (f).
j. Mr. Wheeler withdrew $350 cash from the business to pay personal expenses.

Required:

1. Record the transactions directly in the T-accounts below. Use the transaction letters to identify the amounts in the accounts.
2. Prepare a trial balance on the form provided on the next page.

Cash		
a. 1800	675	b
d 505.50	700	c
i 175	290.50	g
	75	h
	350	j
2480.50	2090.5	
390		

Accounts Payable	
g 290.50	415.50 e
	125

Jon Wheeler, Capital	
	1800 a
	1800

Accounts Receivable	
f 175	175 i
0	

Jon Wheeler, Withdrawals	
j 350	
350	

Prepaid Rent	
b 675	
675	

Revenue from Repairs	
	505.50 d
	175 f
	680.50

Repair Equipment	
c 700	
e 415.50	
1115.50	

Advertising Expense	
h 75	
75	

WHEELER'S REPAIR SHOP
Trial Balance
——————————————————,19—

Cash	390 —		
Prepaid Rent	675 —		
Repair Equipment	1115 50		
Accts Payable		125 —	
John Wheeler, Capital		1800 —	
John Wheeler, Withdrawals	350 —		
Revenue from Repairs		680 50	
Advertising Expense	75		
TOTALS	2605 50	2605 50	

Part IV

Journalize the following transactions and post to the accounts following.

a. On November 5 of the current year Sherry Dale invested $1,500 in cash and office equipment having a fair value of $950 in a real estate agency.
b. On November 6 he purchased for cash office equipment costing $425.

GENERAL JOURNAL

DATE		ACCOUNT TITLES AND EXPLANATION	P.R.	DEBIT	CREDIT
1987					
Nov	5	Cash	1	1500 —	
		Office equip	8	950 —	
		Capital	15		2450 —
		Real Estate Agency investment			
	6	Cash	1		425 —
		Office Equip	B	425 —	
		Bought Office equip	8		

22

GENERAL LEDGER

Cash   Account No. 1

DATE		EXPLANATION	P.R.	DEBIT	CREDIT	BALANCE
Nov	5		GI	1500 —		1500 —
	6		GI		425 —	1075 —

Office Equipment   Account No. 8

DATE		EXPLANATION	P.R.	DEBIT	CREDIT	BALANCE
Nov	5		GI	950 —		950 —
	6		GI	425 —		1375 —

Sherry Dale, Capital   Account No. 15

DATE		EXPLANATION	P.R.	DEBIT	CREDIT	BALANCE
Nov	5		GI		2450 —	2450 —

Solutions for Chapter 2

Part I

Account	16	Journal	18
Account balance	30	Journal page number	8
Account number	6	Ledger	23
Balance column account	3	Mortgage payable	1
Book of final entry	20	Nominal accounts	28
Book of original entry	19	Normal balance of an account	4
Business paper	29	Personal account	9
Capital account	10	Posting	24
Compound journal entry	17	Posting reference (P.R.) column	27
Credit	21	Posting reference numbers	12
Debit	11	Promissory note	22
Double-entry accounting	26	Real accounts	25
Drawing account	13	T-account	7
Folio column	15	Trial balance	2
General journal	5	Withdrawals account	14

Part II

1. a ledger

2. link, journal

3. the difference between the debits and credits entered in it

4. trace the debits and credits

5. increases, decreases

6. to enter in the journal the ledger account number to which the amount was posted. Folio column

7. increases, decreases

8. (a) Determine the balance of each account; (b) List in their ledger order the accounts having balances, with the debit balances in one column and the credit balances in another; (c) Add the debit balances; (d) Add the credit balances; (e) Compare the two totals for equality.

9. credited, debited

10. (a) debit (b) credit (c) credit (d) credit (e) debit (f) credit (g) debit

11. debits, credits. credits, debits

12. entering the balance in the account in red or entering it in black and circling it

13. are not

14. one or more errors have been made

15. debit, credit

16. errors that did not affect the trial balance may have been made

17. the recording accuracy

18. debit, credit, debit, credit

19. Balance, Balance, account's current balance

Part III

Cash			
(a)	1,800.00	(b)	675.00
(d)	505.50	(c)	700.00
(i)	175.00	(g)	290.50
		(h)	75.00
		(j)	350.00

Repair Equipment			
(c)	700.00		
(e)	415.50		

Jon Wheeler, Withdrawals			
(j)	350.00		

Accounts Receivable			
(f)	175.00	(i)	175.00

Accounts Payable			
(g)	290.50	(e)	415.50

Revenue from Repairs			
		(d)	505.50
		(f)	175.00

Prepaid Rent		
(b)	675.00	

Jon Wheeler, Capital			
		(a)	1,800.00

Advertising Expense		
(h)	75.00	

WHEELER'S REPAIR SHOP
Trial Balance, Current Date

Cash	$ 390.00	
Prepaid rent	675.00	
Repair equipment	1,115.50	
Accounts payable		$ 125.00
Jon Wheeler, capital		1,800.00
Jon Wheeler, withdrawals	350.00	
Revenue from repairs		680.50
Advertising expense	75.00	
Totals	$2,605.50	$2,605.50

Part IV

GENERAL JOURNAL   PAGE 1

DATE		ACCOUNT TITLES AND EXPLANATION	P.R.	DEBIT	CREDIT
19— Nov.	5	Cash	1	1 5 0 0 00	
		Office Equipment	8	9 5 0 00	
		Sherry Dale, Capital	15		2 4 5 0 00
		Invested in a real estate agency.			
	6	Office Equipment	8	4 2 5 00	
		Cash	1		4 2 5 00
		Purchased office equipment.			

26

GENERAL LEDGER

Cash — Account No. 1

DATE		EXPLANATION	P.R.	DEBIT	CREDIT	BALANCE
19— Nov.	5		G–1	1 500 00		1 500 00
	6		G–1		425 00	1 075 00

Office Equipment — Account No. 8

DATE		EXPLANATION	P.R.	DEBIT	CREDIT	BALANCE
19— Nov.	5		G–1	950 00		950 00
	6		G–1	425 00		1 375 00

Sherry Dale, Capital — Account No. 15

DATE		EXPLANATION	P.R.	DEBIT	CREDIT	BALANCE
19— Nov.	5		G–1	2 450 00		2 450 00

3

Adjusting the Accounts and Preparing the Statements

Your objectives in studying this chapter should include learning how to:

Explain why the life of a business is divided into accounting periods of equal length and why the accounts of a business must be adjusted at the end of each accounting period.

Prepare adjusting entries for prepaid expenses, accrued expenses, unearned revenues, accrued revenues, and depreciation.

Prepare entries to dispose of accrued revenue and expense items in the new accounting period.

Explain the difference between the cash and accrual bases of accounting.

Explain the importance of comparability in the financial statements of a business, period after period; and tell how the realization principle and the matching principle contribute to comparability.

Define each asset and liability classification appearing on a balance sheet, classify balance sheet items, and prepare a classified balance sheet.

Define or explain the words and phrases listed in the chapter Glossary.

Topical Outline

I. Adjusting the accounting records at the end of an accounting period

    A. Time-period concept—results in a division of the life of a business into time periods of equal length, known as accounting periods, which are of two types:

        1. Calendar year—January 1 to December 31.

        2. Fiscal year—an accounting period of 12 consecutive months.

    B. Accounts that require adjustments are:

        1. Prepaid expenses—expenses that have been paid for in advance of use. These expenses remain assets until they are consumed in the operation of the business.

        2. Depreciation—expiration of a plant asset's quantity of usefulness (an expense just like the expiration of prepaid rent).

        3. Accrued expenses—expenses that have been incurred during an accounting period but have not been paid and recorded because payment is not due.

        4. Unearned revenues—payments received in advance for goods or services to be delivered at a later date.

        5. Accrued revenues—revenues that have been earned during an accounting period but have not been received and recorded because payment is not due.

    C. The adjustment process—recording appropriate adjusting entries and assigning to each accounting period that portion of a transaction's effect applicable to the period, based on:

        1. The realization principle—requires that revenue be assigned to the accounting period in which it is earned.

        2. The matching principle—requires that revenue and expenses be matched.

    D. Bases of accounting are the:

        1. Cash basis—revenues and expenses reported when received or paid in cash.

        2. Accrual basis—revenues reported when earned and expenses matched with revenue.

II. Preparing financial statements

    A. The adjusted trial balance—prepared after adjustments to the accounts have been made.

    B. Classification of balance sheet items

        1. Current assets

            a. Cash

            b. Notes receivable

            c. Accounts receivable

            d. Merchandise inventory

            e. Prepaid insurance

            f. Office supplies

        2. Long-term investments

            a. Stocks

            b. Bonds

            c. Promissory notes

            d. Land held for future expansion

        3. Plant and equipment

            a. Equipment

            b. Buildings

            c. Land

4. Intangible assets

    a. Goodwill
    b. Patents
    c. Trademarks

5. Current liabilities

    a. Notes payable
    b. Accounts payable
    c. Wages payable

6. Long-term liabilities

    a. Mortgage payable
    b. Bonds payable

7. Owners' equity

    a. Single proprietorship
    b. Partnership
    c. Corporation

C. Balance sheet format

1. Account form
2. Report form

Part I

Many of the important ideas and concepts discussed in Chapter 3 are reflected in the following list of key terms. Test your understanding of these terms by matching the appropriate definitions with the terms. Record the number identifying the most appropriate definition in the blank space next to each term.

27	Account form balance sheet	10	Depreciation
26	Accounting period	21	Depreciation expense
23	Accrual basis of accounting	29	Dividend
1	Accrued expense	9	Fiscal year
5	Accrued revenue	22	Intangible asset
15	Accumulated depreciation	13	Matching principle
4	Adjusted trial balance	14	Natural business year
12	Adjusting entries	24	Operating cycle of a business
3	Adjustment process	11	Plant and equipment
17	Cash basis of accounting	2	Prepaid expense
28	Classified balance sheet	16	Report form balance sheet
20	Common stock	8	Retained earnings
25	Contra account	7	Time-period concept
19	Current asset	6	Unadjusted trial balance
30	Current liability	18	Unearned revenue

1. An expense that has been incurred during an accounting period but that has not been paid and recorded because payment is not due.

2. An asset that will be consumed in the operation of a business and that will become an expense as it is consumed.

3. The end-of-period process of recording appropriate adjusting entries to assign revenues to the period in which earned and to match revenues and expenses.

4. A trial balance showing account balances brought up-to-date by recording appropriate adjusting entries.

5. A revenue that has been earned during an accounting period but has not been received and recorded because payment is not due.

6. A trial balance prepared after transactions are recorded but before any adjustments are made.

7. The idea that the life of a business is divisible into time periods of equal length.

8. Stockholders' equity in a corporation resulting from earnings in excess of losses and dividends declared.

9. A period of any 12 consecutive months used as an accounting period.

10. The expiration of a plant asset's "quantity of usefulness."

11. Tangible assets having relatively long lives that are used in the production or sale of other assets or services.

12. Journal entries made to assign revenues to the period in which earned and to match revenues and expenses.

13. The accounting rule that all expenses incurred in earning a revenue be deducted from the revenue in determining net income.

14. Any 12 consecutive months used by a business as an accounting period, at the end of which the activities of the business are at their lowest point.

15. The cumulative amount of depreciation recorded against an asset or group of assets during the entire period of time the asset or assets have been owned.

16. A balance sheet prepared on one page, at the top of which the assets are listed, followed down the page by the liabilities and owner's equity.

17. The accounting basis in which revenues are reported as being earned in the accounting period received in cash and expenses are deducted from revenues in the accounting period in which cash is disbursed in their payment.

18. Payment received in advance for goods or services to be delivered at a later date.

19. Cash or an asset that may reasonably be expected to be realized in cash or be consumed within one year or one operating cycle of the business, whichever is longer.

20. The name given to a corporation's stock when it issues only one kind or class of stock.

21. The expense resulting from the expiration of a plant asset's "quantity of usefulness."

22. An asset having no physical existence but having value because of the rights conferred as a result of its ownership and possession.

23. The accounting basis in which revenues are assigned to the accounting period in which earned regardless of whether or not received in cash, and expenses incurred in earning the revenues are deducted from the revenues regardless of whether or not cash has been disbursed in their payment.

24. The average period of time between the acquisition of merchandise or materials by a business and the realization of cash from the sale of the merchandise or product manufactured from the materials.

25. An account the balance of which is subtracted from the balance of an associated account to show a more proper amount for the item recorded in the associated account.

26. The time interval over which the transactions of a business are recorded and at the end of which its financial statements are prepared.

27. A balance sheet with the assets on the left and the liability and owner's equity items on the right.

28. A balance sheet with assets and liabilities classified into significant groups.

29. A distribution of cash or other assets made by a corporation to its stockholders.

30. A debt or other obligation that must be paid or liquidated within one year or one operating cycle, and the payment or liquidation of which will require the use of presently classified current assets.

Part II

On October 1 of the current year Harold Lloyd began business as a public stenographer. During the month he completed the following transactions:

Oct. 1 Invested $3,000 in the business.
     1 Paid three months' rent in advance on the office space, $1,245.
     1 Purchased office equipment for cash, $925.50.
     2 Purchased on credit office equipment, $700, and office supplies, $75.50.
   31 Completed stenographic work during the month and collected cash, $1,725.
       (Combined into one entry to conserve space.)
   31 Withdrew $725 for personal living expenses.

After the foregoing entries were recorded in the journal and posted, the accounts of Harold Lloyd appeared as follows:

Cash Account No. 1

DATE		EXPLANATION	P.R.	DEBIT	CREDIT	BALANCE
Oct.	1		G–1	3 000 00		3 000 00
	1		G–1		1 245 00	1 755 00
	1		G–1		925 50	829 50
	31		G–2	1 725 00		2 554 50
	31		G–2		725 00	1 829 50

Prepaid Rent Account No. 2

DATE		EXPLANATION	P.R.	DEBIT	CREDIT	BALANCE
Oct.	1		G–1	1 245 00		1 245 00
	31		G2		415 —	830 —

Office Supplies Account No. 3

DATE		EXPLANATION	P.R.	DEBIT	CREDIT	BALANCE
Oct.	2		G–1	75 50		75 50
	31		G2		35 50	40 00

Office Equipment Account No. 4

DATE		EXPLANATION	P.R.	DEBIT	CREDIT	BALANCE
Oct.	1		G–1	925 50		925 50
	2		G–1	700 00		1 625 50

Accumulated Depreciation, Office Equipment — Account No. 5

DATE		EXPLANATION	P.R.	DEBIT	CREDIT	BALANCE
Oct	31		G2		35 —	35 —

Accounts Payable — Account No. 6

DATE		EXPLANATION	P.R.	DEBIT	CREDIT	BALANCE
Oct.	2		G–1		775 50	775 50

Harold Lloyd, Capital — Account No. 7

DATE		EXPLANATION	P.R.	DEBIT	CREDIT	BALANCE
Oct.	1		G–1		3000 00	3000 00

Harold Lloyd, Withdrawals — Account No. 8

DATE		EXPLANATION	P.R.	DEBIT	CREDIT	BALANCE
Oct.	31		G–2	725 00		725 00

Stenographic Revenue — Account No. 9

DATE		EXPLANATION	P.R.	DEBIT	CREDIT	BALANCE
Oct.	31		G–2		1725 00	1725 00

Rent Expense — Account No. 10

DATE		EXPLANATION	P.R.	DEBIT	CREDIT	BALANCE
Oct	31		G2	415 —		415 —

Office Supplies Expense — Account No. 11

DATE		EXPLANATION	P.R.	DEBIT	CREDIT	BALANCE
Oct	31		G2	35 50		35 50

Depreciation Expense, Office Equipment — Account No. 12

DATE		EXPLANATION	P.R.	DEBIT	CREDIT	BALANCE
Oct	31		G2	35 —		35 —

On October 31 Harold Lloyd decided to adjust his accounts and prepare a balance sheet and an income statement. His adjustments were:

a. One month's rent had expired.
b. An inventory of office supplies showed $40 of unused office supplies.
c. The office equipment had depreciated $35 during October.

Required:

1. Prepare and post general journal entries to record the adjustments.
2. After posting the adjusting entries, complete the adjusted trial balance.
3. From the adjusted trial balance complete the income statement and balance sheet.

GENERAL JOURNAL

Page 2

DATE		ACCOUNT TITLES AND EXPLANATION	P.R.	DEBIT	CREDIT
OCT	31	Rent Expense	10	4 15 —	
		Prepaid Rent	2		4 15 —
	31	Office Supplies Expense	11	35 50	
		Office Supplies	3		35 50
	31	Depreciation Expense, Office Equipment	12	35 —	
		Office Equipment, Accumulated Depreciation	5		35 —

HAROLD LLOYD

Adjusted Trial Balance

October 31, 19—

	Debit	Credit
Cash	1829 50	
Prepaid rent	836 —	
Office supplies	40 —	
Office equipment	1625 50	
Accumulated depreciation, office equipment		35 —
Accounts payable		775 50
Harold Lloyd, capital		3000 —
Harold Lloyd, withdrawals	725 —	
Stenographic revenue		1725 —
Rent expense	415 —	
Office supplies expense	35 50	
Depreciation expense, office equipment	35 —	
Totals	5535 50	5535 50

37

HAROLD LLOYD
Income Statement
For Month Ended October 31, 19—

Revenue:							
Stenographic revenue						1725	—
Operating expenses:							
Rent expense	415	—					
Office supplies expense	35	50					
Depreciation expense, office equipment	35	—					
Total operating expenses	485	50					
Net income						1239	50

HAROLD LLOYD
Balance Sheet
October 31, 19—

Assets				
Current Assets:				
Cash	1829	50		
Prepaid rent	830	—		
Office supplies	40	—		
Total current assets			2699	50
Plant and Equipment:				
Office equipment	1625	50		
Less accumulated depreciation	35			
Total plant and equipment			1590	50
Total assets			4290	00
Liabilities				
Current Liabilities:				
Accounts payable	775	50		
Total liabilities			775	50
Owner's Equity				
Harold Lloyd, capital, October 31, 19—		3		
October net income	1239	50		
Less withdrawals	725	00		
Excess of income over withdrawals			514	50
Harold Lloyd, capital, October 1, 19—			3000	—
Total liabilities and owner's equity			4290	00

Part III

a. Blade Company has one employee who earns $72.50 per day. The company operates with monthly accounting periods, and the employee is paid each Friday night for a workweek that begins on Monday. Assume the calendar for October appears as shown on the right and enter the four $362.50 weekly wage payments directly in the T-accounts below. Then enter the adjustment for the wages earned but unpaid on October 31.

	OCTOBER					
S	M	T	W	T	F	S
	1	2	3	4	5	6
7	8	9	10	11	12	13
14	15	16	17	18	19	20
21	22	23	24	25	26	27
28	29	30	31			

Cash		Wages Payable		Wages Expense	
362.50			217.50	362.50	
362.50				362.50	
362.50				362.50	
362.50				362.50	
				217.50	
362.50		217.50			217.50

b. Blade Company's October income statement should show $_____1667.50_____ of

wages expense, and its October 31 balance sheet should show a $____217.50____ liability for wages payable. The wages earned by its employee but unpaid on October 31 are

an example of an ____accrued____ expense.

c. In the space that follows give the general journal entry to record payment of a full week's wages to the Blade Company employee on November 2.

DATE		ACCOUNT TITLES AND EXPLANATION	P.R.	DEBIT	CREDIT
Nov	2	Wages Payable		217 50	
		Wages Expense		145 00	
		Cash			362 50

Part IV

Riverview Properties operates an apartment building. On December 31, at the end of an annual accounting period, its Revenue from Rents account had a $335,500 credit balance, and the Unearned Rents account had a $3,600 credit balance. The following information was available for the year-end adjustments: (a) The credit balance in the Unearned Rents account resulted from a tenant paying his rent for six months in advance beginning on November 1. (b) Also, a tenant in temporary financial difficulties had not paid his rent for the month of December. The amount due was $475.

Required: Enter the necessary adjustments directly in the T-accounts at the top of the next page.

Rents Receivable	Unearned Rents		Revenue from Rents
475	1200	Nov. 1 3,600	Bal. 335,500
		2400	1200
			475
			337,175

After the foregoing adjustments are entered in the accounts, the company's Revenue from Rents account has a $_____337,175_____ balance which should appear on its income statement as revenue earned during the year. Its Unearned Rents account has a $_____2400_____ balance, and this should appear on the company's balance sheet as a _____current Liability (debit)_____. Likewise, the company's Rents Receivable account has a $_____475_____ balance, and this should appear on its balance sheet as a _____current Asset E_____.

Part V

1. Under the cash basis of accounting, the accounting revenues are reported as being earned in the accounting period in which they are received in _____Cash_____; expenses are charged to the period in which _____Cash_____ is disbursed in their payment; and net income for the period is the difference between _____revenue in_____ _____ and _____expenses out_____. Under the accrual basis of accounting, revenues are credited to the period in which _____they're earned_____, expenses are _____matched_____ with revenues, and no consideration is given as to when cash is received or disbursed.

2. Current assets consist of cash and assets that are expected to be realized in cash or (complete definition) _____Sold or used w/in 1 yr or 1 business cycle whichever longer_____
_____
_____

3. The basic purpose behind the adjustment process described in this chapter, the recognition principle, and the matching principle is _____to make economic/financial comparisons accurate from period to period._____
_____

Solutions for Chapter 3

Part I

Part II

Oct. 31	Rent Expense	415.00	
	Prepaid Rent		415.00
31	Office Supplies Expense	35.50	
	Office Supplies		35.50
31	Depreciation Expense, Office Equipment	35.00	
	Accumulated Depreciation, Office Equipment		35.00

Cash

Date		Debit	Credit	Balance
Oct.	1	3,000.00		3,000.00
	1		1,245.00	1,755.00
	1		925.50	819.50
	31	1,725.00		2,554.50
	31		725.00	1,829.50

Accounts Payable

Date		Debit	Credit	Balance
Oct.	2		775.50	775.50

Harold Lloyd, Capital

Date		Debit	Credit	Balance
Oct.	1		3,000.00	3,000.00

Prepaid Rent

		Debit	Credit	Balance
Oct.	1	1,245.00		1,245.00
	31		415.00	830.00

Harold Lloyd, Withdrawals

		Debit	Credit	Balance
Oct.	31	725.00		725.00

Office Supplies

		Debit	Credit	Balance
Oct.	2	75.50		75.50
	31		35.50	40.00

Stenographic Revenue

		Debit	Credit	Balance
Oct.	31		1,725.00	1,725.00

Office Equipment

		Debit	Credit	Balance
Oct.	1	925.50		925.50
	2	700.00		1,625.50

Rent Expense

		Debit	Credit	Balance
Oct.	31	415.00		415.00

Accumulated Depr., Office Equipment

		Debit	Credit	Balance
Oct.	31		35.00	35.00

Office Supplies Expense

		Debit	Credit	Balance
Oct.	31	35.50		35.50

Depr. Expense, Office Equipment

		Debit	Credit	Balance
Oct.	31	35.00		35.00

HAROLD LLOYD
Adjusted Trial Balance
October 31, 19—

Cash	$1,829.50	
Prepaid rent	830.00	
Office supplies	40.00	
Office equipment	1,625.50	
Accumulated depreciation, office equipment		$ 35.00
Accounts payable		775.50
Harold Lloyd, capital		3,000.00
Harold Lloyd, withdrawals	725.00	
Stenographic revenue		1,725.00
Rent expense	415.00	
Office supplies expense	35.50	
Depreciation expense, office equipment	35.00	
Totals	$5,535.50	$5,535.50

HAROLD LLOYD
Income Statement
For Month Ended October 31, 19—

Revenue:

Stenographic revenue $1,725.00

Operating expenses:

Rent expense	$ 415.00	
Office supplies expense	35.50	
Depreciation expense, office equipment	35.00	
Total operating expenses		485.50
Net income		$1,239.50

HAROLD LLOYD
Balance Sheet
October 31, 19—

Assets

Current Assets:

Cash	$1,829.50	
Prepaid rent	830.00	
Office supplies	40.00	
Total current assets		$2,699.50

Plant and Equipment:

Office equipment	$1,625.50	
Less accumulated depreciation	35.00	
Total plant and equipment		1,590.50
Total assets		$4,290.00

Liabilities

Current Liabilities:

Accounts payable	$ 775.50
Total liabilities	$ 775.50

Owner's Equity

Harold Lloyd, capital, October 1, 19—		$3,000.00
October net income	$1,239.50	
Less withdrawals	725.00	
Excess of income over withdrawals		514.50
Harold Lloyd, capital, October 31, 19—		3,514.50
Total liabilities and owner's equity		$4,290.00

Part III

a.

Cash				Wages Payable				Wages Expense		
Oct.	5	362.50				Oct. 31	217.50	Oct.	5	362.50
	12	362.50							12	362.50
	19	362.50							19	362.50
	26	362.50							26	362.50
									31	217.50

b. $1,667.50; $217.50; accrued

c. Nov. 2 Wages Expense 145.00

                    Wages Payable 217.50

                    Cash 362.50

Part IV

Rents Receivable			Unearned Rents				Revenue from Rents		
Dec. 31	475		Dec. 31	1,200	Nov. 1	3,600	Bal.		335,500
							Dec. 31		1,200
							31		475

Revenue from Rents, $337,175
Unearned Rents, $2,400, current liability
Rents Receivable, $475, current asset

Part V

1. cash, cash, revenue receipts, expense disbursements, earned, matched

2. be sold or consumed within one year or within one operating cycle of the business, whichever is longer

3. to make the information on accounting statements comparable from period to period

4

The Work Sheet and Closing the Accounts of Proprietorships, Partnerships, and Corporations

Your objectives in studying this chapter should include learning how to:

Explain why a work sheet is prepared and be able to prepare a work sheet for a service-type business.

Explain why it is necessary to close the revenue and expense accounts at the end of each accounting period.

Prepare entries to close the temporary accounts of a service business and prepare a post-closing trial balance to test the accuracy of the end-of-period adjusting and closing procedures.

Explain the nature of the retained earnings item on corporation balance sheets.

Explain why a corporation with a deficit cannot pay a legal dividend.

Prepare entries to close the Income Summary account of a corporation and to record the declaration and payment of a dividend.

List the steps in the accounting cycle in the order in which they are completed.

Define or explain the words and phrases listed in the chapter Glossary.

Topical Outline

I. The work sheet and adjusting entries

    A. A work sheet is prepared at the end of each accounting period to:

        1. Reflect the effects of adjustments before adjusting entries are made.
        2. Provide the information used in preparing financial statements by sorting adjusted account balances into appropriate income statement and balance sheet columns.
        3. Calculate and prove the mathematical accuracy of net income.

    B. To prepare a work sheet:

        1. List all accounts contained in the unadjusted trial balance.
        2. Make adjusting entries in appropriate columns.
        3. Combine amounts in unadjusted trial balance columns and adjustment columns and carry these amounts to adjusted trial balance columns.
        4. Add adjusted trial balance columns to prove their equality.
        5. Sort amounts into balance sheet or income statement columns.
        6. Determine net income (or loss) by taking the difference between debit and credit totals of income statement columns and balance the balance sheet columns by adding net income (or loss).
        7. Journalize and post adjusting entries.

II. Closing entries

    A. Closing entries are made to:

        1. Transfer the effects of revenues and expenses to the capital account.
        2. Bring the temporary (revenue, expense, withdrawal, and Income Summary) account balances to zero, so that revenues and expenses in the next accounting period can be properly recorded.

    B. Closing the accounts

        1. Revenue accounts, which have credit balances, are cleared and closed by debiting the account and crediting Income Summary.
        2. Expense accounts, which have debit balances, are cleared and closed by crediting the account and debiting Income Summary.
        3. The balance of the Income Summary account is transferred to the proprietor's capital account.
        4. The withdrawals account is closed to the proprietor's capital account.

III. Accounting for partnerships and corporations

    A. Partnership accounting is like accounting for a single proprietorship, except:

        1. Separate withdrawals and capital accounts are kept for each partner.
        2. The Income Summary account is closed with a compound journal entry to allocate each partner's share of income (or loss).

    B. Corporation accounting is also like accounting for a single proprietorship, except:

        1. There are two kinds of stockholders' equity accounts:

            a. Contributed capital accounts (such as Common Stock)
            b. Retained Earnings account

        2. The Income Summary account is closed to the Retained Earnings account.
        3. Dividend payments reduce the balance of the Retained Earnings account.

IV. The accounting cycle—the sequence of accounting procedures followed each accounting period:

   A. Journalizing transactions
   B. Posting
   C. Preparing a trial balance
   D. Preparing a work sheet
   E. Preparing the statements
   F. Adjusting the ledger accounts
   G. Closing the temporary accounts
   H. Preparing a post-closing trial balance

Part I

Many of the important ideas and concepts discussed in Chapter 4 are reflected in the following list of key terms. Test your understanding of these terms by matching the appropriate definitions with the terms. Record the number identifying the most appropriate definition in the blank space next to each term.

3	Accounting cycle	6	Deficit
10	Closing entries	11	Income Summary account
4	Closing procedures	2	Post-closing trial balance
8	Contributed capital	1	Stockholders of record
9	Date of declaration	5	Temporary accounts
7	Date of payment	14	Working papers
13	Date of record	12	Work sheet

1. A corporation's stockholders according to its records.

2. A trial balance prepared after closing entries are posted.

3. The accounting steps that recur each accounting period in the life of a business and that begin with the recording of transactions and proceed through posting the recorded amounts, preparing a trial balance, preparing a work sheet, preparing the financial statements, preparing and posting adjusting and closing entries, and preparing a post-closing trial balance.

4. The preparation and posting of closing entries and the preparation of the post-closing trial balance.

5. The revenue, expense, Income Summary, and withdrawals accounts.

6. A negative amount of retained earnings.

7. Date for the payment of a dividend.

8. Stockholders' equity in a corporation resulting among other ways from amounts invested in the corporation by its stockholders.

9. Date on which a dividend is declared.

10. Entries made to close and clear the revenue and expense accounts and to transfer the amount of the net income or loss to a capital account or accounts or to the Retained Earnings account.

11. The account used in the closing procedures to summarize the amounts of revenues and expenses, and from which the amount of the net income or loss is transferred to the owner's capital account in a single proprietorship, the partners' capital accounts in a partnership, or the Retained Earnings account in a corporation.

12. A working paper used by an accountant to bring together in an orderly manner the information used in preparing the financial statements and the adjusting and closing entries.

13. Date on which the stockholders who are to receive a dividend are determined.

14. The memoranda, analyses, and other informal papers prepared by accountants and used as a basis for the more formal reports given to clients.

Part II

Complete the following by filling in the blanks.

1. A work sheet is prepared after all transactions are recorded but before

    ~~x the balance sheet & income statement~~

    ✓ the adjustments are entered into the accts.
    .

2. Revenue accounts have credit balances; consequently, to clear and close a revenue account and make it show a zero balance, the revenue account is __debited__ and the Income Summary account is __credited__ for the amount of the balance.

3. In sorting the amounts in the Adjusted Trial Balance columns of a work sheet to the proper Income Statement or Balance Sheet columns, two decisions are involved in sorting each item. The decisions are: (a) __which statement it goes on__ and (b) __which column it goes in (debit or credit)__ .

4. Expense accounts have debit balances; therefore, expense accounts are __credited__ and the Income Summary account is __debited__ in closing the expense accounts.

5. In preparing a work sheet for a concern, its unadjusted ledger account balances are entered in the __first 2 columns__ of the work sheet form, after which the __adjustments__ are entered in the Adjustments columns. Next, the trial balance amounts and the amounts in the Adjustments columns are combined to secure a(n) __adjusted trial balance__ in the Adjusted Trial Balance columns.

6. A work sheet is a tool of the accountant, usually prepared in pencil, and used to—
    (a) __adjust the accts before actually entering the adjustments into the accts.__ ,
    (b) __sort the adjusted acct balances into columns for the statement they appear on.__ ,
    (c) __clear the math__
    .

7. Only balance sheet accounts should have balances appearing on the post-closing trial balance because the balances of all revenue and expense accounts are reduced to __0__ in the closing procedure.

8. A corporation has two kinds of stockholders' equity accounts, called __contributed capital__ and __retained earnings__ .

50

9. Closing entries are necessary because if at the end of an accounting period the revenue and expense accounts are to show only one period's revenues and expenses, they must begin the period with _____ 0 _____ balances, and closing entries cause the revenue and expense accounts to begin a new period with _____ 0 _____ _____ balances.

10. Closing entries accomplish two purposes: (1) they cause all _____ expense & revenue _____ _____ accounts to begin the new accounting period with zero balances, and (2) they transfer the net effect of the past period's _____ revenue _____, _____ expense _____, and withdrawal transactions to the owner's capital account.

Part III

The unfinished year-end work sheet of Homer's Home Shop appears on the next page.

Required:

1. Complete the work sheet using the following adjustments information:
   a. A $725 inventory of shop supplies indicates that $1,037 of shop supplies have been used during the year.
   b. The shop equipment has depreciated $475 during the year.
   c. On December 31, wages of $388 have been earned by the one employee but are unpaid because payment is not due.

2. After completing the work sheet, prepare the year-end adjusting and closing entries.

3. Post the adjusting and closing entries to the accounts that appear in skeletonized form beginning on page 54.

4. After posting the adjusting and closing entries, prepare a post-closing trial balance.

HOMER'S HOME SHOP

Work Sheet for Year Ended December 31, 19—

ACCOUNT TITLES	TRIAL BALANCE DR.	TRIAL BALANCE CR.	ADJUSTMENTS DR.	ADJUSTMENTS CR.	ADJUSTED TRIAL BALANCE DR.	ADJUSTED TRIAL BALANCE CR.	INCOME STATEMENT DR.	INCOME STATEMENT CR.	BALANCE SHEET DR.	BALANCE SHEET CR.
Cash	2,875 00				2875				2875	
Accounts receivable	2,000 00				2000				2000	
Shop supplies	1,762 00			a 1037	725				725	
Shop equipment	5,125 00				5125				5125	
Accumulated depreciation, shop equipment		725 00		b 475		1200				1200
Accounts payable		575 00				575				575
Homer Tonely, capital		5,500 00				5500				5500
Homer Tonely, withdrawals	30,000 00				30000				30000	
Revenue from repairs		55,785 00				55785		55785		
Rent expense	2,500 00				2500		2500			
Wages expense	18,250 00		c 388		18638		18638			
Miscellaneous expenses	73 00				73		73			
	62,585 00	62,585 00								
Shop supplies expense			a 1037		1037		1037			
Depreciation expense, shop equipment			b 475		475		475			
Wages payable				c 388		388				388
			1900	1900	63448	63448	22723	55785	40725	33062
INCOME							33062			33062
							55785	55785	40725	40725

DATE		ACCOUNT TITLES AND EXPLANATION	P.R.	DEBIT	CREDIT
19 DEC	31	Shop Supplies Expense	✓	1037 —	
		Shop Supplies	✓		1037 —
		Adjustment			
DEC	31	Depreciation Expense, Shop Equipment	✓	475 —	
		Accumulated Deprec., Shop Equip	✓		475 —
		Adjustment			
	31	Wages Expense	✓	388 —	
		Wages Payable	✓		388 —
		Accrued Wages			
	31	Revenue from Repairs	✓	55785 —	
		Income Summary	✓		55785 —
	31	Income Summary	✓	22723 —	
		Rent Expense	✓		2500 —
		Wages Expense	✓		18638 —
		Misc. Exp.	✓		73 —
		Shop Supplies Exp.	✓		1037 —
		Depr. Exp., Shop Equip.	✓		475 —
	31	Income Summary	✓	33062 —	
		Homer Tonely, Capital	✓		33062 —
	31	Homer Tonely, Capital	✓	30000 —	
		Homer Tonely, Withdrawals	✓		30000 —

Cash

Date	Debit	Credit	Balance
Dec. 31			2,875.00

Accounts Receivable

Date	Debit	Credit	Balance
Dec. 31			2,000.00

Shop Supplies

Date	Debit	Credit	Balance
Dec. 31			1,762.00
31		1037.—	725
			725

Shop Equipment

Date	Debit	Credit	Balance
Dec. 31			5,125.00

Accumulated Depr., Shop Equipment

Date	Debit	Credit	Balance
Dec. 31		475	725.00
31		475	1200
			1200

Accounts Payable

Date	Debit	Credit	Balance
Dec. 31			575.00

Wages Payable

Date	Debit	Credit	Balance
Dec 31		388	388

Homer Tonely, Capital

Date	Debit	Credit	Balance
Dec. 31			5,500.00
31		33062	38,562
31	30000		8,562

Homer Tonely, Withdrawals

Date	Debit	Credit	Balance
Dec. 31			30,000.00
31		30000	0

Income Summary

Date	Debit	Credit	Balance
31		55785	55785
31	22723		33062
31	33062		0

Revenue from Repairs

Date	Debit	Credit	Balance
Dec. 31			55,785.00
31	55785		0

Rent Expense

Date	Debit	Credit	Balance
Dec. 31			2,500.00
31		2500	0

Wages Expense

Date	Debit	Credit	Balance
Dec. 31			18,250.00
31	388		18,638
31		18,638	0

Miscellaneous Expenses

Date	Debit	Credit	Balance
Dec. 31			73.00
31		73	0

Shop Supplies Expense

Date	Debit	Credit	Balance
Dec 31	1037		1037
31		1037	0

Depr. Expense, Shop Equipment

Date	Debit	Credit	Balance
Dec 31	475.—		475.—
31		475	0

54

HOMER'S HOME SHOP
Post-Closing Trial Balance
December 31, 19—

	Debit	Credit
Cash	2875	
Accounts receivable	2000	
Shop supplies	725	
Shop equipment	5125	
Accumulated depreciation, shop equipment		1200
Accounts payable		575
Wages payable		388
Homer Tonely, capital		8562
Totals	10725	10725

Part IV

Prepare journal entries to record the following events relating to Slater Company.

1. Slater Company sold 15,000 shares of $25 par common stock for $375,000.
2. In making closing entries, the net income for the year amounted to $50,000.
3. Slater Company declared $15,500 of dividends to be paid in cash to common stockholders.
4. Slater Company paid the dividends declared in (3).

GENERAL JOURNAL

DATE	ACCOUNT TITLES AND EXPLANATION	P.R.	DEBIT	CREDIT
	Cash		375000	
	Capital - Contributed - Common Stock			375000
	Income Summary		50000	
	Retained Earnings			50000
	Retained Earnings		15500	
	Divd. - Payable			15500
	Dividends Payable		15500	
	Cash			15500

Part I

Part II

1. the adjustments are entered in the accounts

2. debited, credited

3. (a) Is the item a debit or a credit?
   (b) On which statement does it appear?

4. credited, debited

5. first two money columns, or Trial Balance columns; adjustments, adjusted trial balance

6. (a) achieve the effect of adjusting the accounts before entering the adjustments in the accounts,
   (b) sort the adjusted account balances into columns according to the statement on which they appear, and
   (c) calculate and prove the mathematical accuracy of the net income or loss.

7. zero

8. contributed capital accounts, retained earnings accounts

9. zero, zero

10. revenue and expense, revenue, expense

HOMER'S HOME SHOP
Work Sheet for Year Ended December 31, 19—

	Trial Balance Dr.	Trial Balance Cr.	Adjustments Dr.	Adjustments Cr.	Adjusted Trial Balance Dr.	Adjusted Trial Balance Cr.	Income Statement Dr.	Income Statement Cr.	Balance Sheet Dr.	Balance Sheet Cr.
Cash	2,875				2,875				2,875	
Accounts receivable	2,000				2,000				2,000	
Shop supplies	1,762			(a) 1,037	725				725	
Shop equipment	5,125				5,125				5,125	
Accumulated depreciation, shop equipment		725		(b) 475		1,200				1,200
Accounts payable		575				575				575
Homer Tonely, capital		5,500				5,500				5,500
Homer Tonely, withdrawals	30,000				30,000				30,000	
Revenue from repairs		55,785				55,785		55,785		
Rent expense	2,500				2,500		2,500			
Wages expense	18,250		(c) 388		18,638		18,638			
Miscellaneous expenses	73				73		73			
	62,585	62,585								
Shop supplies expense			(a) 1,037		1,037		1,037			
Depreciation expense, shop equipment			(b) 475		475		475			
Wages payable				(c) 388		388				388
			1,900	1,900	63,448	63,448	22,723	55,785	40,725	7,663
Net income							33,062			33,062
							55,785	55,785	40,725	40,725

Dec. 31	Shop Supplies Expense	1,037	
	Shop Supplies		1,037
31	Depr. Expense, Shop Equipment	475	
	Accumulated Depr., Shop Equipment		475
31	Wages Expense	388	
	Wages Payable		388

Dec. 31	Revenue from Repairs	55,785	
	Income Summary		55,785
31	Income Summary	22,723	
	Rent Expense		2,500
	Wages Expense		18,638
	Miscellaneous Expenses		73
	Shop Supplies Expense		1,037
	Depr. Expense, Shop Equipment		475
31	Income Summary	33,062	
	Homer Tonely, Capital		33,062
31	Homer Tonely, Capital	30,000	
	Homer Tonely, Withdrawals		30,000

GENERAL LEDGER

Cash 1

Date	Debit	Credit	Balance
Dec. 31			2,875.00

Accounts Receivable 2

Date	Debit	Credit	Balance
Dec. 31			2,000.00

Shop Supplies 3

Date	Debit	Credit	Balance
Dec. 31			1,762.00
31		1,037.00	725.00

Shop Equipment 4

Date	Debit	Credit	Balance
Dec. 31			5,125.00

Accumulated Depr., Shop Equipment 5

Date	Debit	Credit	Balance
Dec. 31			725.00
31		475.00	1,200.00

Accounts Payable 6

Date	Debit	Credit	Balance
Dec. 31			575.00

Wages Payable 7

Date	Debit	Credit	Balance
Dec. 31		388.00	388.00

Homer Tonely, Capital 8

Date	Debit	Credit	Balance
Dec. 31			5,500.00
31		33,062.00	38,562.00
31	30,000.00		8,562.00

Homer Tonely, Withdrawals 9

Date	Debit	Credit	Balance
Dec. 31			30,000.00
31		30,000.00	–0–

Income Summary 10

Date	Debit	Credit	Balance
Dec. 31		55,785.00	55,785.00
31	22,723.00		33,062.00
31	33,062.00		–0–

Revenue from Repairs 11

Date	Debit	Credit	Balance
Dec. 31			55,785.00
31	55,785.00		–0–

Rent Expense 12

Date	Debit	Credit	Balance
Dec. 31			2,500.00
31		2,500.00	–0–

Wages Expense 13

Date	Debit	Credit	Balance
Dec. 31			18,250.00
31	388.00		18,638.00
31		18.638.00	–0–

Miscellaneous Expenses 14

Date	Debit	Credit	Balance
Dec. 31			73.00
31		73.00	–0–

Shop Supplies Expense 15

Date	Debit	Credit	Balance
Dec. 31	1,037.00		1,037.00
31		1,037.00	–0–

Depr. Expense, Shop Equipment 16

Date	Debit	Credit	Balance
Dec. 31	475.00		475.00
31		475.00	–0–

HOMER'S HOME SHOP
Post-Closing Trial Balance
December 31, 19—

Cash	$ 2,875	
Accounts receivable	2,000	
Shop supplies	725	
Shop equipment	5,125	
Accumulated depreciation, shop equipment		$ 1,200
Accounts payable		575
Wages payable		388
Homer Tonely, Capital		8,562
	$10,725	$10,725

Part IV

1. Cash	375,000.00	
Common Stock		375,000.00
2. Income Summary	50,000.00	
Retained Earnings		50,000.00
3. Retained Earnings	15,500.00	
Common Dividend Payable		15,500.00
4. Common Dividend Payable	15,500.00	
Cash		15,500.00

5

Accounting for a Merchandising Concern

Your objectives in studying this chapter should include learning how to:

Explain the nature of each item entering into the calculation of cost of goods sold and be able to calculate cost of goods sold and gross profit from sales.

Prepare a work sheet and the financial statements for a merchandising business using a periodic inventory system and organized as either a corporation or a single proprietorship.

Prepare adjusting and closing entries for a merchandising business organized as either a corporation or a single proprietorship.

Define or explain the words and phrases listed in the chapter Glossary.

Topical Outline

I. Accounting for a merchandising concern differs from accounting for a service enterprise

    A. Net income of a service organization is fees (or commissions) earned less operating expenses.

    B. Net income of a merchandising concern is sales revenue less cost of goods sold and operating expenses.

    C. Revenue from sales less cost of goods sold equals gross profit from sales—the "profit" before operating expenses are deducted.

II. Revenue from sales is:

    A. Gross sales—total cash and credit sales before any deductions.

    B. Less sales returns and allowances—the gross sales value of merchandise returned by customers and deductions from the sales price granted to customers for unsatisfactory goods.

    C. Less sales discounts—reductions in the amount customers must pay, which are granted if payment is made early.

III. Cost of goods sold and the periodic inventory system

    A. Merchandise inventory at the end of one period is the beginning inventory of the next period.

    B. Cost of merchandise purchased includes the gross purchase price plus transportation-in, less purchases (cash) discounts and less purchases returns and allowances.

    C. Cost of goods sold is calculated as the cost of beginning inventory plus the cost of merchandise purchased less the cost of ending inventory.

    D. Inventory losses from shrinkage, spoilage, and theft are automatically included in the cost of goods sold.

IV. Classified income statement of a merchandising concern has three sections:

    A. Revenue section

    B. Cost of goods sold section

    C. Operating expenses section

V. Preparing a work sheet for a merchandising concern

    A. The titles of the accounts to be used are entered in the Account Titles column.

    B. The unadjusted account balances are entered in the Trial Balance columns.

    C. All necessary adjustments are entered in the Adjustments columns.

    D. The adjusted amounts are sorted to the proper financial statement columns.

    E. Cost of goods sold appears on the work sheet as follows:

        1. Beginning inventory, purchases, and transportation-in amounts appear in the Income Statement debit column.

        2. The amounts of the ending inventory, purchases returns and allowances, and purchases discounts appear in the Income Statement credit column.

    F. The formal financial statements are prepared using the information contained in the completed work sheet.

VI. Retained earnings statement for a corporation

    A. Prepared in addition to an income statement and a balance sheet.

    B. Reports changes in the corporation's retained earnings that have occurred during the period.

VII. Adjusting and closing entries

    A. Adjusting entries for merchandising companies include similar entries as are used in a service business.

See pg 47 → To close: 1) Close everything on Income Statement a) DR b) CR to Income S
2) Close Income Summary to capital (profits/Losses)
3) Close Captal to withdrawals

B. Closing entries

1. Before closing entries are posted, the Merchandise Inventory account shows beginning-of-period inventory as a debit balance.
2. The first closing entry includes a credit to Merchandise Inventory for the amount of the beginning inventory.
3. The second closing entry includes a debit to Merchandise Inventory for the amount of the ending inventory.

VIII. Financial statements in addition to the balance sheet

A. Income statement—may be designed as:

1. Classified (multiple-step) statement in which items are grouped in significant categories
2. Single-step statement

B. Retained earnings statement of a corporation

1. Shows beginning retained earnings, plus net income, less dividends declared, which equals ending retained earnings.
2. May be combined with income statement.

C. Statement of changes in financial position—shows where a corporation secured funds and where it used the funds.

IX. Debit and credit memoranda

A. Used by a company to communicate with a customer or supplier.
B. Tells the customer or supplier that the amount the company expects to receive or pay is being changed.

X. Trade discounts

A. Deductions from list (or catalog) price to arrive at invoice price
B. Not entered in the accounts of seller or purchaser

Part I

Many of the important ideas and concepts discussed in Chapter 5 are reflected in the following list of key terms. Test your understanding of these terms by matching the appropriate definitions with the terms. Record the number identifying the most appropriate definition in the blank space next to each term.

18	Cash discount		20	Merchandise inventory
14	Credit memorandum		6	Multiple-step income statement
11	Credit period		15	Periodic inventory system
10	Credit terms		2	Perpetual inventory system
5	Debit memorandum		13	Purchases discounts
16	Discount period		9	Retained earnings statement
7	EOM		4	Sales discounts
22	FOB		19	Selling expenses
21	General and administrative expenses		17	Single-step income statement
1	Gross profit from sales		3	Trade discount
8	List price		12	Transportation-in

1. Net sales minus cost of goods sold.

2. An inventory system in which an individual record is kept for each product of the units on hand at the beginning, the units purchased, the units sold, and the new balance after each purchase or sale.

3. The discount that may be deducted from a catalog list price to determine the invoice price of goods.

4. Discounts given on sales of merchandise.

5. A memorandum sent to notify its recipient that the business sending the memorandum has in its records debited the account of the recipient.

6. An income statement on which cost of goods sold and the expenses are subtracted in steps to arrive at net income.

7. An abbreviation meaning "end of month."

8. The catalog or other listed price from which a trade discount is deducted in arriving at the invoice price for goods.

9. A statement which reports changes in a corporation's retained earnings that occurred during an accounting period.

10. The agreed terms upon which credit is granted in the sale of goods or services.

11. The agreed period of time for which credit is granted and at the end of which payment is expected.

12. Freight, express, or other transportation costs on merchandise purchased for resale.

13. Discounts taken on merchandise purchased for resale.

14. A memorandum sent to notify its recipient that the business sending the memorandum has in its records credited the account of the recipient.

15. An inventory system in which periodically, at the end of each accounting period, the cost of the unsold goods on hand is determined by counting units of each product on hand, multiplying the count for each product by its cost, and adding costs of the various products.

16. The period of time in which a cash discount may be taken.

17. An income statement on which cost of goods sold and the expenses are added together and subtracted in one step from revenue to arrive at net income.

18. A deduction from the invoice price of goods allowed if payment is made within a specified period of time.

19. The expenses of preparing and storing goods for sale, promoting sales, making sales, and if a separate delivery department is not maintained, the expenses of delivering goods to customers.

20. The unsold merchandise on hand at a given time.

21. The general office, accounting, personnel, and credit and collection expenses.

22. The abbreviation for "free on board," which is used to denote that goods purchased are placed on board the means of transportation at a specified geographic point free of any loading and transportation charges to that point.

Part II

Below is the Valentine Variety Store work sheet for the year ended December 31, 1987. The adjustments and the Adjustments columns have been omitted from the work sheet to simplify it, and it has been completed through the Adjusted Trial Balance columns. Sort the adjusted trial balance amounts into the proper Income Statement and Balance Sheet columns and finish the work sheet. The December 31, 1987, inventory is $15,000.

VALENTINE VARIETY STORE
Work Sheet, December 31, 1987

ACCOUNT TITLES	TRIAL BALANCE DR.	TRIAL BALANCE CR.	ADJUSTED TRIAL BALANCE DR.	ADJUSTED TRIAL BALANCE CR.	INCOME STATEMENT DR.	INCOME STATEMENT CR.	BALANCE SHEET DR.	BALANCE SHEET CR.
Cash	4,000 00		4,000 00				4000	
Merchandise inventory	13,000 00		13,000 00		13000	15000	15000	
Other assets	8,000 00		8,000 00				8000	
Liabilities		4,000 00		4,000 00				4000
Violet Valentine, capital		22,300 00		22,300 00				22,300
Violet Valentine, withdrawals	10,000 00		10,000 00				10000	
Sales		80,000 00		80,000 00		80,000		
Sales returns	600 00		600 00		600			
Purchases	48,500 00		48,500 00		48,500			
Purchases returns		400 00		400 00		400		
Purchases discounts		900 00		900 00		900		
Transportation-in	2,500 00		2,500 00		2500			
Selling expenses	13,000 00		13,000 00		13 000			
Gen. and admin. expenses	8,000 00		8,000 00		8000			
	107,600 00	107,600 00	107,600 00	107,600 00	85,600	96,300	37000	26,300
Net income					10 700			10 700
					96,300	96,300	37000	37000

Part III

After finishing the work sheet, use the information in its Income Statement columns to complete the following income statement.

VALENTINE VARIETY STORE

Income Statement

For the Year Ended December 31, 1987

Revenue:				
Sales			80000	
Less: Sales returns			600	
Net sales				79400
Cost of goods sold:				
Merchandise inventory, January 1, 1987			13000	
Purchases		48500		
Less: Purchases returns $ 400				
Purchases discounts 900		1300		
Net purchases		47200		
Add: Transportation-in		2500		
Cost of goods purchased			49700	
Goods available for sale			62700	
Merchandise inventory, December 31, 1987			15000	
Cost of goods sold				47700
Gross profit from sales				31700
Operating expenses:				
Selling expenses			13000	
General and administrative expenses			8000	
Total operating expenses				21000
Net income				10700

68

Part IV

Prepare the closing entries for Valentine Variety Store. Do not make explanations, but skip a line after each entry.

DATE		ACCOUNT TITLES AND EXPLANATION	P.R.	DEBIT	CREDIT
DEC	31	Income Summary		85600	
		Sales Returns			600
		Purchases			48500
		Transportation - In			2500
		Selling Exp			13000
		Gen & Admin Exp			8000
		Merchandise Inv			13000
	31	Sales		80000	
		Purchases Returns		400	
		Purchases Discounts		900	
		Merchandise Inv		15000	
		Income Summary			96300
	31	Income Summary		10700	
		Violet Valentine, Capital			10700
	31	Violet Valentine, Capital		10000	
		Violet Valentine, Withdrawals			10000

Part V

Below is the Merchandise Inventory account of Valentine Variety Store as it appeared before the 1987 closing entries were posted. Note that its $13,000 debit balance shows the amount of the January 1, 1987, beginning inventory which was posted to the account when the closing entries were made at the end of the previous year, 1986. From the closing entries that were journalized in Part IV, post the appropriate amounts to the Merchandise Inventory account below.

Merchandise Inventory   Account No. 115

DATE		EXPLANATION	P.R.	DEBIT	CREDIT	BALANCE
1986 Dec.	31		G-3	13 0 0 0 00		13 0 0 0 00
1987 Dec	31		G-9		13 0 00	0 —
	31		G-9	15 0 00		15 0 00

69

Part VI

1. The periodic inventory system gets its name from the fact that when it is in use, it is periodically necessary (at the end of each accounting period) to take an _____ *inventory* _____ of the unsold merchandise remaining on hand in order to learn the cost of the _____ *goods / merchandise* _____ that has been sold.

2. Trade discounts _____ (are, (are not)) credited to the Purchases Discounts account.

3. After the work sheet is completed, the amount of the ending inventory is taken into the accounts by means of a(n) _____ *closing* _____ entry.

4. A store received a credit memorandum from a wholesaler for unsatisfactory merchandise the store had returned for credit. The store should record the memorandum with a _____ (debit, (credit)) to its Purchases Returns and Allowances account and a _____ ((debit), credit) to its Accounts Payable account.

5. The two common systems for determining cost of goods sold are the _____ *perpetual* _____ inventory system and the _____ *periodic* _____ inventory system. The _____ *periodic* _____ inventory system is the one most commonly used in stores selling a volume of relatively low-priced items.

Part I

Cash discount	18	Merchandise inventory	20
Credit memorandum	14	Multiple-step income statement	6
Credit period	11	Periodic inventory system	15
Credit terms	10	Perpetual inventory system	2
Debit memorandum	5	Purchases discounts	13
Discount period	16	Retained earnings statement	9
EOM	7	Sales discounts	4
FOB	22	Selling expenses	19
General and administrative expenses	21	Single-step income statement	17
Gross profit from sales	1	Trade discount	3
List price	8	Transportation-in	12

Part II

VALENTINE VARIETY STORE
Work Sheet, December 31, 1987

	Adjusted Trial Balance		Income Statement		Balance Sheet	
	Dr.	Cr.	Dr.	Cr.	Dr.	Cr.
Cash	4,000				4,000	
Merchandise inventory	13,000		13,000	15,000	15,000	
Other assets	8,000				8,000	
Liabilities		4,000				4,000
Violet Valentine, capital		22,300				22,300
Violet Valentine, withdrawals	10,000				10,000	
Sales		80,000		80,000		
Sales returns	600		600			
Purchases	48,500		48,500			
Purchases returns		400		400		
Purchases discounts		900		900		
Transportation-in	2,500		2,500			
Selling expenses	13,000		13,000			
General and administrative expenses	8,000		8,000			
	107,600	107,600	85,600	96,300	37,000	26,300
Net income			10,700			10,700
			96,300	96,300	37,000	37,000

Part III

VALENTINE VARIETY STORE
Income Statement
For the Year Ended December 31, 1987

Revenue:
Sales $80,000
   Less: Sales returns 600
Net sales $79,400
Cost of goods sold:
Merchandise inventory, January 1, 1987 .... $13,000
Purchases $48,500
   Less: Purchases returns $400
      Purchases discounts 900   1,300
Net purchases $47,200
   Add: Transportation-in 2,500
Cost of goods purchased 49,700
Goods available for sale $62,700
Merchandise inventory, December 31, 1987 15,000
Cost of goods sold 47,700
Gross profit from sales $31,700
Operating expenses:
Selling expenses $13,000
General and administrative expenses 8,000
Total operating expenses 21,000
Net income $10,700

Part IV

Dec. 31	Income Summary	85,600.00	
	Sales Returns		600.00
	Purchases		48,500.00
	Transportation-in		2,500.00
	Selling Expenses		13,000.00
	General and Administrative Expenses		8,000.00
	Merchandise Inventory		13,000.00
31	Sales	80,000.00	
	Purchases Returns	400.00	
	Purchases Discounts	900.00	
	Merchandise Inventory	15,000.00	
	Income Summary		96,300.00
31	Income Summary	10,700.00	
	Violet Valentine, Capital		10,700.00
31	Violet Valentine, Capital	10,000.00	
	Violet Valentine, Withdrawals		10,000.00

Part V

			DATE		EXPLANATION	P.R.	DEBIT				CREDIT				BALANCE				

Merchandise Inventory — Account No. 115

DATE		EXPLANATION	P.R.	DEBIT	CREDIT	BALANCE
1986						
Dec.	31		G–3	13 000 00		13 000 00
1987						
Dec.	31		G–8		13 000 00	- 0 -
	31		G–9	15 000 00		15 000 00

Part VI

1. inventory, merchandise

2. are not

3. closing

4. credit, debit

5. periodic, perpetual, periodic

6

Accounting Systems

Your objectives in studying this chapter should include learning how to:

Explain how columnar journals save posting labor.

State what type of transaction is recorded in each columnar journal described in the chapter.

Explain how a controlling account and its subsidiary ledger operate and give the rule for posting to a subsidiary ledger and its controlling account.

Record transactions in and post from the columnar journals described.

Explain how the accuracy of the account balances in the Accounts Receivable and Accounts Payable Ledgers is proved and be able to make such a proof.

Describe how data is processed in a large business.

Define or explain the words and phrases listed in the chapter Glossary.

Topical Outline

I. An accounting system

    A. Consists of the business papers, records, reports, and procedures used by a business in recording transactions and reporting their effects.

    B. Involves:

        1. Gathering transaction information into source documents.

        2. Classifying and recording the data in accounting records.

        3. Preparing timely summary reports to management and other interested parties.

II. Subsidiary ledgers

    A. Information about the amounts purchased and the amounts owed by each customer requires a separate accounts receivable account for each customer. These accounts are usually maintained in a subsidiary ledger.

    B. Each subsidiary ledger (whether it is an Accounts Receivable Ledger, an Accounts Payable Ledger, or other supplemental ledger) is represented by a controlling account in the General Ledger.

    C. A subsidiary ledger is periodically proved by totaling the balances of the accounts in the ledger and comparing the total to the controlling account's balance.

III. Special journals

    A. Reduce writing and posting labor, by grouping similar transactions together and recording them in one place and periodically posting totals accumulated.

    B. Examples:

        1. Sales Journal—records all credit (no cash) sales

            a. Individual entries in the Sales Journal are posted to the accounts in the subsidiary Accounts Receivable Ledger.

            b. The column total of the Sales Journal is posted as a debit to Accounts Receivable and a credit to Sales in the General Ledger.

        2. Cash Receipts Journal—records all cash receipts, such as

            a. Cash from charge customers

            b. Cash sales

            c. Miscellaneous receipts of cash

        3. Purchases Journal—records all credit purchases (but no cash purchases) of merchandise

        4. Cash Disbursements Journal—records all payments of cash except those made from petty cash. (A reimbursement of petty cash is, however, recorded in the Cash Disbursements Journal.)

        5. General Journal—provided even when special journals are used to allow the recording of entries which do not fit under any of the special journals, such as

            a. Adjusting entries

            b. Closing entries

            c. Other entries such as credit purchases of items other than merchandise

IV. Machine methods and computerized data processing

    A. A variety of machines, such as electronic bookkeeping machines, are available to reduce the labor of maintaining an accounting system.

    B. Computerized data processing systems are replacing electronic bookkeeping machine systems. These systems involve the use of a computer which is programmed to rapidly calculate and store information used in a business.

Part I

Many of the important ideas and concepts discussed in Chapter 6 are reflected in the following list of key terms. Test your understanding of these terms by matching the appropriate definitions with the terms. Record the number identifying the most appropriate definition in the blank space next to each term.

8	Accounting system	16	Crossfoot
3	Accounts Payable Ledger	12	Foot
9	Accounts Receivable Ledger	15	General Ledger
17	Batch processing	6	Online processing
13	Check Register	18	Schedule of accounts payable
1	Columnar journal	14	Schedule of accounts receivable
11	Computer	2	Special journal
4	Computer program	7	Subsidiary ledger
10	Controlling account	5	Time sharing

1. A book of original entry having columns, each of which is designated as the place for entering specific data about each transaction of a group of similar transactions.

2. A book of original entry that is designed and used for recording only a specified type of transaction.

3. A subsidiary ledger having an account for each creditor.

4. A set of instructions that are entered in a computer and that specify the operations the computer is to perform.

5. A process by which several users of a computer, each having an input-output device, can input data into a single computer and, as processing time becomes available, have their data processed and transmitted back to their output device.

6. A mode of computer operation in which the program and required data are maintained in the computer so that as new data are entered, they are processed instantly.

7. A group of accounts other than general ledger accounts which show the details underlying the balance of a controlling account in the General Ledger.

8. The business papers, records, reports, and procedures used by a business in recording transactions and reporting their effects.

9. A subsidiary ledger having an account for each customer.

10. A General Ledger account the balance of which (after posting) equals the sum of the balances of the accounts in a related subsidiary ledger, thereby proving the sum of those subsidiary account balances.

11. A complex electronic machine that has the capacity to store a program of instructions and data, process the data rapidly according to the instructions, and prepare reports showing the results of the processing operation.

12. To add a column of numbers.

13. A book of original entry for recording payments by check.

14. A list of customer account balances with the total.

15. The ledger containing the financial statement accounts of a business.

16. To add the debit column totals of a journal, add the credit column totals, and then compare the sums to prove that total debits equal total credits.

17. A mode of computer operation in which a program and data are entered in the computer, processed, and removed from the computer before the next program and data are entered.

18. A list of creditor account balances with the total.

Part II

Complete the following by filling in the blanks.

1. The posting principle upon which a subsidiary ledger and its controlling account operate requires that the controlling account be debited for an amount or amounts equal to the sum of _____ to the subsidiary ledger and that the controlling account be credited for an amount or amounts equal to the sum of _____ _____ to the subsidiary ledger.

2. When a company records sales returns with general journal entries, the credit of an entry recording such a return is posted to two different accounts. This does not cause the trial balance to be out of balance because _____ _____.

3. Cash sales _____ (are, are not) normally recorded in the Sales Journal.

4. Orders for store supplies or office supplies should be recorded in a _____ _____.

5. When a subsidiary Accounts Receivable Ledger is maintained, the equality of the debits and credits posted to the General Ledger is proved by preparing _____ _____. At the same time the balances of the customer accounts in the Accounts Receivable Ledger are proved by preparing _____ _____.

Part III

Below are eight transactions completed by McGuff Company on September 30 of this year. Following the transactions are the company's journals with a representation of its September transactions recorded therein.

Requirement One: Record the eight transactions in the company's journals.

Sept. 30 Received an $808.50 check from Ted Clark in full payment of the September 20, $825 sale, less the $16.50 discount.
   30 Received a $550 check from a tenant in payment of his October rent.
   30 Sold merchandise to Inez Smythe on credit, Invoice No. 655, $1,675.
   30 Received merchandise and an invoice dated September 28, terms 2/10, n/60 from Johnson Company, $4,000.
   30 Purchased store equipment on account from Olson Company, terms n/10, EOM, $950.
   30 Issued Check No. 525 to Kerry Meadows in payment of her $650 salary.
   30 Issued Check No. 526 for $1,715 to Olson Company in full payment of its September 20 invoice, less a $35 discount.
   30 Cash sales for the first half of the month totaled $9,450.50.

GENERAL JOURNAL
Page 17

DATE	ACCOUNT TITLES AND EXPLANATION	P.R.	DEBIT	CREDIT

SALES JOURNAL
Page 8

DATE		ACCOUNT DEBITED	INVOICE NUMBER	P.R.	AMOUNT
19—					
Sept.	3	N. R. Boswell	651	√	1 8 7 5 00
	15	Inez Smythe	652	√	1 5 0 0 00
	20	Ted Clark	653	√	8 2 5 00
	24	N. R. Boswell	654	√	2 2 5 0 00

PURCHASES JOURNAL
Page 8

DATE		ACCOUNT CREDITED	DATE OF INVOICE	TERMS	P.R.	AMOUNT
19—						
Sept.	8	Johnson Company	9/6	2/10, n/60	√	3 7 5 0 00
	22	Olson Company	9/20	2/10, n/60	√	1 7 5 0 00
	24	Olson Company	9/22	2/10, n/60	√	5 6 2 5 00

CASH RECEIPTS JOURNAL

DATE		ACCOUNT CREDITED	EXPLANATION	P.R.	OTHER ACCOUNTS CREDIT	ACCOUNTS RECEIVABLE CREDIT	SALES CREDIT	SALES DISCOUNTS DEBIT	CASH DEBIT
19—									
Sept.	1	Rent Earned	Tenant's September rent	711	550 00				550 00
	13	N. R. Boswell	Full payment of account	√		1 875 00		37 50	1 837 50
	15	Sales	Cash sales	√			9 000 00		9 000 00

CASH DISBURSEMENTS JOURNAL

DATE		CH. NO.	PAYEE	ACCOUNT DEBITED	P.R.	OTHER ACCOUNTS DEBIT	ACCOUNTS PAYABLE DEBIT	PURCHASES DISCOUNT CREDIT	CASH CREDIT
19—									
Sept.	15	212	Kerry Meadows	Salaries Expense	611	650 00			650 00
	16	213	Johnson Company	Johnson Company	√		3 750 00	75 00	3 675 00

Requirement Two: The individual postings from the journals of McGuff Company through September 29 have been made. Complete the individual postings from the journals.

Requirement Three: Foot and crossfoot the journals and make the month-end postings.

Requirement Four: Complete the trial balance on page 84 and prove the subsidiary ledgers by preparing schedules of accounts receivable and accounts payable.

ACCOUNTS RECEIVABLE LEDGER

N. R. Boswell

2200 Falstaff Street

DATE		EXPLANATION	P.R.	DEBIT	CREDIT	BALANCE
19— Sept.	3		S–8	1 875 00		1 875 00
	13		R–9		1 875 00	–0–
	24		S–8	2 250 00		2 250 00

Ted Clark

10765 Catonsville Avenue

DATE		EXPLANATION	P.R.	DEBIT	CREDIT	BALANCE
19— Sept.	20		S–8	825 00		825 00

Inez Smythe

785 Violette Circle

DATE		EXPLANATION	P.R.	DEBIT	CREDIT	BALANCE
19— Sept.	15		S–8	1 500 00		1 500 00

ACCOUNTS PAYABLE LEDGER

Johnson Company

118 E. Seventh Street

DATE		EXPLANATION	P.R.	DEBIT	CREDIT	BALANCE
19— Sept.	8		P–8		3 750 00	3 750 00
	16		D–7	3 750 00		–0–

Olson Company

788 Hazelwood Avenue

DATE		EXPLANATION	P.R.	DEBIT	CREDIT	BALANCE
19— Sept.	22		P–8		1 750 00	1 750 00
	24		P–8		5 625 00	7 375 00

GENERAL LEDGER

Cash   Account No. 111

DATE		EXPLANATION	P.R.	DEBIT	CREDIT	BALANCE

Accounts Receivable   Account No. 112

DATE		EXPLANATION	P.R.	DEBIT	CREDIT	BALANCE

Store Equipment   Account No. 133

DATE		EXPLANATION	P.R.	DEBIT	CREDIT	BALANCE

Accounts Payable   Account No. 212

DATE		EXPLANATION	P.R.	DEBIT	CREDIT	BALANCE

Sales   Account No. 411

DATE		EXPLANATION	P.R.	DEBIT	CREDIT	BALANCE

Sales Discounts   Account No. 412

DATE		EXPLANATION	P.R.	DEBIT	CREDIT	BALANCE

Purchases   Account No. 511

DATE		EXPLANATION	P.R.	DEBIT	CREDIT	BALANCE

Purchases Discounts   Account No. 512

DATE		EXPLANATION	P.R.	DEBIT	CREDIT	BALANCE

Salaries Expense   Account No. 611

DATE		EXPLANATION	P.R.	DEBIT	CREDIT	BALANCE
19— Sept.	15		D–7	650 00		650 00

Rent Earned   Account No. 711

DATE		EXPLANATION	P.R.	DEBIT	CREDIT	BALANCE
19— Sept.	1		R–9		550 00	550 00

MCGUFF COMPANY
Trial Balance
September 30, 19—

Cash		
Accounts receivable		
Store equipment		
Accounts payable		
Sales		
Sales discounts		
Purchases		
Purchases discounts		
Salaries expense		
Rent earned		

MCGUFF COMPANY
Schedule of Accounts Receivable
September 30, 19—

MCGUFF COMPANY
Schedule of Accounts Payable
September 30, 19—

Part I

Accounting system 8
Accounts Payable Ledger 3
Accounts Receivable Ledger 9
Batch processing 17
Check Register 13
Columnar journal 1
Computer 11
Computer program 4
Controlling account 10

Crossfoot 16
Foot 12
General Ledger 15
Online processing 6
Schedule of accounts payable 18
Schedule of accounts receivable 14
Special journal 2
Subsidiary ledger 7
Time sharing 5

Part II

1. the debits posted, the credits posted
2. only the balance of one of the accounts, the Accounts Receivable account, appears on the trial balance.
3. are not
4. Purchases Journal
5. a trial balance, a schedule of accounts receivable

Part III

Sept. 30 Store Equipment 133   950.00
           Accounts Payable—Olson Company .... 212/√   950.00

85

SALES JOURNAL

Page 8

DATE		ACCOUNT DEBITED	INVOICE NUMBER	P.R.	AMOUNT
19— Sept.	3	N. R. Boswell	651	√	1 8 7 5 00
	15	Inez Smythe	652	√	1 5 0 0 00
	20	Ted Clark	653	√	8 2 5 00
	24	N. R. Boswell	654	√	2 2 5 0 00
	30	Inez Smythe	655	√	1 6 7 5 00
	30	Accounts Receivable, Dr., Sales, Cr.			8 1 2 5 00

PURCHASES JOURNAL

Page 8

DATE		ACCOUNT CREDITED	DATE OF INVOICE	TERMS	P.R.	AMOUNT
19— Sept.	8	Johnson Company	9/6	2/10, n/60	√	3 7 5 0 00
	22	Olson Company	9/20	2/10, n/60	√	1 7 5 0 00
	24	Olson Company	9/22	2/10, n/60	√	5 6 2 5 00
	30	Johnson Company	9/28	2/10, n/60	√	4 0 0 0 00
	30	Purchases, Dr., Accounts Payable, Cr.				1 5 1 2 5 00

CASH RECEIPTS JOURNAL

Page 9

DATE		ACCOUNT CREDITED	P.R.	OTHER ACCOUNTS CREDIT	ACCOUNTS RECEIVABLE CREDIT	SALES CREDIT	SALES DISCOUNTS DEBIT	CASH DEBIT
19— Sept.	1	Rent Earned	711	5 5 0 00				5 5 0 00
	13	N. R. Boswell	√		1 8 7 5 00		3 7 50	1 8 3 7 50
	15	Sales	√			9 0 0 0 00		9 0 0 0 00
	30	Ted Clark	√		8 2 5 00		1 6 50	8 0 8 50
	30	Rent Earned	711	5 5 0 00				5 5 0 00
	30	Sales	√			9 4 5 0 50		9 4 5 0 50
	30	Totals		1 1 0 0 00	2 7 0 0 00	18 4 5 0 50	5 4 00	22 1 9 6 50

DATE	CH. NO.	PAYEE	ACCOUNT DEBITED	P.R.	OTHER ACCOUNTS DEBIT	ACCOUNTS PAYABLE DEBIT	PURCHASES DISCOUNT CREDIT	CASH CREDIT
19— Sept. 15	523	Kerry Meadows	Salaries Expense	611	650 00			650 00
16	524	Johnson Company	Johnson Company	√		3 750 00	75 00	3 675 00
30	525	Kerry Meadows	Salaries Expense	611	650 00			650 00
30	526	Olson Company	Olson Company	√		1 750 00	35 00	1 715 00
30		Totals			1 300 00	5 500 00	110 00	6 690 00

GENERAL LEDGER

Cash

Date	Debit	Credit	Balance
Sept. 30	22,196.50		22,196.50
30		6,690.00	15,506.50

Sales Discounts

Date	Debit	Credit	Balance
Sept. 30	54.00		54.00

Accounts Receivable

Date	Debit	Credit	Balance
Sept. 30	8,125.00		8,125.00
30		2,700.00	5,425.00

Purchases

Date	Debit	Credit	Balance
Sept. 30	15,125.00		15,125.00

Store Equipment

Date	Debit	Credit	Balance
Sept. 30	950.00		950.00

Purchases Discounts

Date	Debit	Credit	Balance
Sept. 30		110.00	110.00

Accounts Payable

Date	Debit	Credit	Balance
Sept. 30		950.00	950.00
30		15,125.00	16,075.00
30	5,500.00		10,575.00

Salaries Expense

Date	Debit	Credit	Balance
Sept. 15	650.00		650.00
30	650.00		1,300.00

Sales

Date	Debit	Credit	Balance
Sept. 30		8,125.00	8,125.00
30		18,450.50	26,575.50

Rent Earned

Date	Debit	Credit	Balance
Sept. 1		550.00	550.00
30		550.00	1,100.00

ACCOUNTS PAYABLE LEDGER

Johnson Company

Date	Debit	Credit	Balance
Sept. 8		3,750.00	3,750.00
16	3,750.00		–0–
30		4,000.00	4,000.00

Olson Company

Date	Debit	Credit	Balance
Sept. 22		1,750.00	1,750.00
24		5,625.00	7,375.00
30		950.00	8,325.00
30	1,750.00		6,575.00

ACCOUNTS RECEIVABLE LEDGER

N. R. Boswell

Date	Debit	Credit	Balance
Sept. 3	1,875.00		1,875.00
13		1,875.00	–0–
24	2,250.00		2,250.00

Inez Smythe

Date	Debit	Credit	Balance
Sept. 15	1,500.00		1,500.00
30	1,675.00		3,175.00

Ted Clark

Date	Debit	Credit	Balance
Sept. 20	825.00		825.00
30		825.00	–0–

MCGUFF COMPANY
Trial Balance
September 30, 19—

Cash	$15,506.50	
Accounts receivable	5,425.00	
Store equipment	950.00	
Accounts payable		$10,575.00
Sales		26,575.50
Sales discounts	54.00	
Purchases	15,125.00	
Purchases discounts		110.00
Salaries expense	1,300.00	
Rent earned		1,100.00
Totals	$38,360.50	$38,360.50

MCGUFF COMPANY
Schedule of Accounts Receivable
September 30, 19—

N. R. Boswell	$ 2,250.00
Inez Smythe	3,175.00
Total Accounts Receivable	$ 5,425.00

MCGUFF COMPANY
Schedule of Accounts Payable
September 30, 19—

Johnson Company	$ 4,000.00
Olson Company	6,575.00
Total Accounts Payable	$10,575.00

7

Accounting for Cash

Your objectives in studying this chapter should include learning how to:

Explain why internal control procedures are needed in a large concern and state the broad principles of internal control.

Describe internal control procedures to protect cash received from cash sales, cash received through the mail, and cash disbursements.

Explain the operation of a petty cash fund and be able to make entries to establish and reimburse a petty cash fund.

Explain why the bank balance and the book balance of cash are reconciled and be able to prepare such a reconciliation.

Tell how recording invoices at net amounts helps gain control over cash discounts taken and be able to account for invoices recorded at net amounts.

Define or explain the words and phrases listed in the chapter Glossary.

Topical Outline

I. Internal control procedures—designed to protect assets from fraud and theft

   A. Seven broad principles of internal control are:

      1. Responsibilities should be clearly established.
      2. Adequate records should be maintained.
      3. Assets should be insured and employees bonded.
      4. Record-keeping and custody should be separated.
      5. Responsibility for related transactions should be divided.
      6. Mechanical devices should be used whenever practicable.
      7. Regular and independent reviews should be conducted.

   B. Computers and internal control

      1. Provide rapid access to large quantities of information.
      2. Reduce processing errors.
      3. Allow more extensive testing of records.
      4. May limit hard evidence of processing steps.
      5. Separation of duties must be maintained.

   C. Internal control for cash should include procedures for protecting:

      1. Cash receipts

         a. Cash from cash sales
         b. Cash received through the mail

      2. Cash disbursements

   D. Voucher system—used to control the incurrence and payment of obligations requiring the disbursement of cash; involves the use of:

      1. Purchase requisitions
      2. Purchase orders
      3. Invoices
      4. Receiving reports
      5. Invoice approval forms
      6. Vouchers

II. Accounting for cash

   A. Petty cash fund—used to avoid writing checks for small amounts.

      1. Petty cash is debited only when the fund is established or increased.
      2. Petty cash receipts are retained by the petty cashier to account for the amounts expended.
      3. When the petty cash fund is reimbursed, an entry is made to debit the expenses or other items paid for with petty cash and to credit Cash for the amount reimbursed to the petty cash fund.

   B. Cash Over and Short account—an income statement item showing the cash shortages or overages resulting from making change.
   C. Reconciling the bank balance

      1. A bank reconciliation proves the accuracy of both the depositor's records and those of the bank.
      2. Items that may cause a difference between the bank statement balance and a depositor's book balance of cash:

         a. Outstanding checks
         b. Unrecorded deposits
         c. Charges for services and uncollectible items

        d. Collections made by the bank for the depositor

        e. Errors

   3. Steps in reconciling the bank balance:

        a. Compare deposits listed on the bank statement with deposits shown in the accounting records.

        b. Determine whether other credits on bank statement (interest, etc.) have been recorded in the books.

        c. Compare canceled checks listed on bank statement with actual checks returned with statement.

        d. Compare previous month's outstanding checks with canceled checks listed on this month's bank statement.

        e. Compare canceled checks listed on bank statement with checks recorded in books since last reconciliation.

        f. Note any unrecorded debits shown on bank statement; e.g., check printing charges, NSF checks, service charges.

        g. Prepare reconciliation.

        h. Make journal entries for any unrecorded debits or credits appearing on the bank statement.

III. Other internal control procedures

  A. Recording purchases

    1. Gross method—purchases recorded at gross amount of invoices

    2. Net method—purchases recorded at net amount of invoices (gross amount less cash discount); provides better control over purchase discounts.

Part I

Many of the important ideas and concepts discussed in Chapter 7 are reflected in the following list of key terms. Test your understanding of these terms by matching the appropriate definitions with the terms. Record the number identifying the most appropriate definition in the blank space next to each term.

17	Bank reconciliation	16	Purchase order
10	Canceled checks	12	Purchase requisition
13	Cash Over and Short account	1	Receiving report
3	Discounts lost	18	Reconcile
8	Gross method of recording invoices	2	Vendee
14	Internal controls system	5	Vendor
6	Invoice	7	Voucher
11	Invoice approval form	9	Voucher Register
19	Net method of recording invoices	15	Voucher system
4	Outstanding checks		

1. A form used within a business to notify the proper persons of the receipt of goods ordered and of the quantities and condition of the goods.

2. The purchaser of something.

3. Cash discounts offered but not taken.

4. Checks that have been written, recorded, and sent or given to payees but that have not been received, paid, and canceled by the bank.

5. The individual or enterprise selling something.

6. A document, prepared by a vendor, on which are listed the items sold, the sales prices, the customer's name, and the terms of sale.

7. A business paper used in summarizing a transaction and approving it for recording and payment.

8. A method of recording purchases by which offered cash discounts are not deducted from the invoice price in determining the amount to be recorded.

9. A book of original entry in which approved vouchers are recorded.

10. Checks that have been punched or stamped by the bank to show they have been paid.

11. A document on which the accounting department notes that it has performed each step in the process of checking an invoice and approving it for recording and payment.

12. A business form used within a business to ask the purchasing department of the business to buy needed items.

13. An income statement account in which are recorded cash overages and cash shortages arising from making change.

14. The procedures adopted by a business to encourage adherence to prescribed managerial policies, to protect its assets from waste, fraud, and theft, and to ensure accurate and reliable accounting data.

15. An accounting system used to control the incurrence and payment of obligations requiring the disbursement of cash.

16. A business form used in placing an order for the purchase of goods from a vendor.

17. An analysis explaining the difference between an enterprise's book balance of cash and its bank statement balance.

18. To account for the difference between two amounts.

19. A method of recording purchases by which offered cash discounts are deducted from the invoice price in determining the amount to be recorded.

Part II

Complete the following by filling in the blanks.

1. A depositor's book balance of cash is reconciled with its bank statement balance in order to prove _the accuracy_ of both the depositor's records and those of the bank.

2. A(n) _Invoice approval_ form is used by the accounting department in checking and approving an invoice for recording and payment.

3. A petty cash fund is established to avoid _writing many small checks_ _____.

4. If the size of the petty cash fund remains unchanged, the Petty Cash account _____ (is, is not) debited in the entry to replenish the petty cash fund.

5. Control of a small business is commonly gained through the direct supervision and active participation of the _owner-manager_ in the affairs and activities of the business. However, as a business grows, it becomes necessary for the manager to delegate responsibilities and rely on _internal controls_ rather than personal contact in controlling the affairs and activities of the business.

6. A properly designed internal control system encourages adherence to prescribed managerial policies; and it also (a) _promotes operational efficiencies_ _____; (b) _protects the assets from waste, fraud & theft_ _____; and (c) _ensures accurate & reliable acctg data_ _____.

7. A good system of internal control for cash requires a _separation_ of duties so that the people responsible for handling cash and for its custody are not the same people who _record it_ _____. It also requires that all cash receipts be deposited in the bank _daily_ _____ and that all payments, except petty cash payments, be made by _check_.

94

8. Good internal control follows certain broad principles. These principles are:

   (a) Responsibilities should be clearly established, and in every situation _____ _a different person_____ should be made responsible for each task.

   (b) Adequate records should be maintained since they provide an important means of protecting _assetts_____.

   (c) Assets should be ___insured_____ and employees _bonded_____.

   (d) Record-keeping for assets and ___custody_____ of assets should be separated.

   (e) Responsibility for related transactions should be _divided_____ so that the work of one department or individual may act as a check on the work of others, but ___duplication_____ in work should be avoided.

   (f) Mechanical devices ___should be used_____ where practicable.

   (g) Regular and independent ___audits/reviews_____ of internal control procedures should be conducted.

9. A voucher system gains control over cash disbursements by providing a routine which

   (a) permits only authorized ___people & departments_____ to incur obligations that will result in cash disbursements; (b) establishes procedures for incurring such obligations and for their ___verification, approval & recording_____; and

   (c) permits checks to be issued only in payment of ___properly verified &___ _approved_____ obligations.

10. A ___purchase requisition_____ is commonly used by a selling department to notify the purchasing department of items which the selling department wishes the purchasing department to purchase.

11. The business form commonly used by the purchasing department of a large company instead of a letter to order merchandise is called a(n) ___purchase order_____ _____.

12. The form used by the receiving department to notify the accounting department that a shipment has arrived and that the items of the shipment have been counted and inspected is called a(n) ___receiving report._____.

Part III

On November 5 of the current year Cullen Company drew Check No. 23 for $50 to establish a petty cash fund. Lon Dial, an office clerk, was appointed petty cashier.

1. Give the cash disbursements journal entry to record the establishment of the fund.

CASH DISBURSEMENTS JOURNAL

DATE 198–	CH. NO.	PAYEE	ACCOUNT DEBITED	P.R.	OTHER ACCOUNTS DEBIT	CASH CREDIT
NOV 5	23	Lon Dial, Petty Cashier	Petty Cash		50 00	50

After making a payment from petty cash on November 25, the petty cashier noted that there was only $2.50 cash remaining in the fund. The cashier prepared the following list of expenditures from the fund and requested that the fund be replenished.

Nov. 9 Express freight on merchandise purchased .... $ 9.75
12 Miscellaneous expense to clean office 10.00
15 Office supplies 3.50
18 Delivery of merchandise to customer 8.00
23 Miscellaneous expense for collect telegram 3.25
25 Express freight on merchandise purchased 13.00

Check No. 97 in the amount of $47.50 was drawn to replenish the fund.

2. In the Cash Disbursements Journal below give the entry to record the check replenishing the petty cash fund.

CASH DISBURSEMENTS JOURNAL

DATE	CH. NO.	PAYEE	ACCOUNT DEBITED	P.R.	OTHER ACCOUNTS DEBIT	CASH CREDIT
NOV 25	97	Lon Dial, Petty Cashier	Transportation-In		22 75	
			Misc Exp.		13 25	
			Office Supplies		3 50	
			Delivery Exp		8 00	47 5

Part IV

Below preceded by identifying letters are seven items that would cause Xavier Sales Company's book balance of cash to differ from its bank statement balance.

a. A service charge made by the bank.
b. A check listed as outstanding on the previous month's reconciliation and that is still outstanding.
c. A customer's check returned by the bank marked "Not Sufficient Funds."
d. A deposit consisting solely of checks which was mailed to the bank on the last day of November and is unrecorded on the November bank statement.
e. A check paid by the bank at its correct $190 amount but recorded in error in the Check Register at $109.
f. An unrecorded credit memorandum indicating the bank had collected a note receivable for Xavier Sales Company and deposited the proceeds in the company's account.
g. A check written during November and not yet paid and returned by the bank.

96

Required:

1. Indicate where each item would appear on Xavier Sales Company's bank reconciliation by placing its identifying letter in the parentheses in the proper section of the form below.

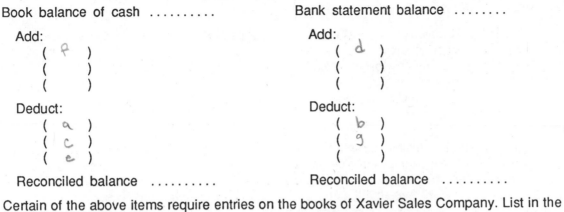

XAVIER SALES COMPANY
Bank Reconciliation
November 30, 19—

Book balance of cash ....   Bank statement balance ....

Add: Add:
   (f)   (d)
   ( )   ( )
   ( )   ( )

Deduct: Deduct:
   (a)   (b)
   (c)   (g)
   (e)   ( )

Reconciled balance ....   Reconciled balance ....

2. Certain of the above items require entries on the books of Xavier Sales Company. List in the parentheses below the identifying letters of these items.

   (a)   (e)   ( )
   (c)   (f)   ( )

Part V

On May 8 a company that records invoices at net amounts received a shipment of merchandise having a $3,750 invoice price. Attached to the merchandise was the invoice which was dated May 6, terms 2/10, n/60, FOB the vendor's warehouse. The vendor, Vee Company, had prepaid the shipping charges on the goods, $125, adding the amount to the invoice and bringing its total to $3,875. The invoice was recorded and filed in error for payment on May 26. Give in general journal form the entries to record the (1) purchase, (2) discovery on May 26 of the discount lost, and (3) payment of the invoice on July 5. Do not give explanations but skip a line between entries.

DATE, 19—		ACCOUNT TITLES AND EXPLANATION	P.R.	DEBIT	CREDIT
MAY	8	Purchases		3675	
		Transport - In		125	
		Accts Payable - Vee Co			3800
	26	Discount Lost		75	
		Accts Payable - Vee Co			75
Jul	5	Accts Payable - Vee Co.		3875	
		Cash			3875

Part VI (based on the Appendix at the end of the chapter)

On this page and the next page are the Check Register and Voucher Register of Nero Sales Company, a concern that records invoices at gross amounts. Both registers have a representation of cash disbursement transactions recorded therein. Following are six additional transactions of the company.

Required: (1) Record the transactions in the registers. (2) Crossfoot the registers and post.
(3) Prepare a schedule of unpaid vouchers.

Feb. 21 Prepared Voucher No. 8 payable to WSID Radio Station for advertising expense, $175. Issued Check No. 7 in payment of the voucher.

24 Prepared Voucher No. 9 payable to Office Sales Company for the purchase of office equipment, $500, terms n/10 EOM.

25 Prepared Voucher No. 10 payable to Radion Company for the purchase of merchandise, $1,875, terms 2/10, n/60.

26 Issued Check No. 8 in payment of Voucher No. 7 less a 2% discount.

28 Prepared Voucher No. 11 payable to Neal Realty Company for the March rent, $500. Issued Check No. 9 in payment of the voucher.

28 Prepared Voucher No. 12 payable to Payroll for sales salaries, $625; and office salaries, $375. Issued Check No. 10 in payment of the voucher. Cashed the check and paid the employees.

CHECK REGISTER
Page 1

DATE		PAYEE	VCHR. NO.	CH. NO.	VOUCHERS PAYABLE DR.	PURCHASES DISCOUNT CR.	CASH CR.
Feb.	1	Union Truck Company	2	1	60 00		60 00
	8	Inter-City Wholesale Company	1	2	2 000 00	40 00	1 960 00
	13	Alpha Supply Company	3	3	250 00		250 00
	15	Payroll	5	4	1 000 00		1 000 00
	17	Treadwell and Son	4	5	700 00	14 00	686 00
	18	Morning Gazette	6	6	75 00		75 00

VOUCHER REGISTER

	DATE		VCHR. NO.	PAYEE	WHEN AND HOW PAID		VOUCHERS PAYABLE CREDIT		PURCHASES DEBIT		TRANS-PORTA-TION–IN DEBIT		
					DATE	CH. NO.							
1	Feb.	1	1	Inter-City Wholesale Co.	Feb. 8	2	2,000	00	2,000	00			1
2		1	2	Union Truck Company	1	1	60	00			60	00	2
3		5	3	Alpha Supply Company	13	3	250	00					3
4		9	4	Treadwell and Son	17	5	700	00	675	00	25	00	4
5		15	5	Payroll	15	4	1,000	00					5
6		18	6	Morning Gazette	18	6	75	00					6
7		18	7	Dale Brothers			1,250	00	1,250	00			7
8													8
9													9
10													10
11													11
12													12
13													13
14													14

VOUCHER REGISTER

	SALES SALARIES EXPENSE DEBIT		ADVER-TISING EXPENSE DEBIT		OFFICE SALARIES EXPENSE DEBIT		OTHER ACCOUNTS DEBIT				
							ACCOUNT NAME	P.R.	AMOUNT		
1											1
2											2
3							Store Supplies		250	00	3
4											4
5	625	00			375	00					5
6			75	00							6
7											7
8											8
9											9
10											10
11											11
12											12
13											13
14											14

Cash   Account No. 111

DATE	EXPLANATION	P.R.	DEBIT	CREDIT	BALANCE

Store Supplies   Account No. 115

DATE	EXPLANATION	P.R.	DEBIT	CREDIT	BALANCE

Office Equipment   Account No. 137

DATE	EXPLANATION	P.R.	DEBIT	CREDIT	BALANCE

Vouchers Payable   Account No. 212

DATE	EXPLANATION	P.R.	DEBIT	CREDIT	BALANCE

Purchases   Account No. 511

DATE	EXPLANATION	P.R.	DEBIT	CREDIT	BALANCE

Purchases Discounts   Account No. 513

DATE	EXPLANATION	P.R.	DEBIT	CREDIT	BALANCE

Transportation-in   Account No. 514

DATE	EXPLANATION	P.R.	DEBIT	CREDIT	BALANCE

Rent Expense   Account No. 611

DATE	EXPLANATION	P.R.	DEBIT	CREDIT	BALANCE

Sales Salaries Expense

Account No. 612

DATE	EXPLANATION	P.R.	DEBIT	CREDIT	BALANCE

Advertising Expense

Account No. 613

DATE	EXPLANATION	P.R.	DEBIT	CREDIT	BALANCE

Office Salaries Expense

Account No. 652

DATE	EXPLANATION	P.R.	DEBIT	CREDIT	BALANCE

NERO SALES COMPANY
Schedule of Vouchers Payable
February 28, 19—

Voucher Number	Payee	Amount

Part I

Part II

1. the accuracy

2. invoice approval

3. writing numerous checks for small amounts

4. is not

5. owner-manager, a system of internal control

6. (a) promotes operational efficiencies; (b) protects the business assets from waste, fraud, and theft; and (c) ensures accurate and reliable accounting data

7. separation, keep the cash records, intact each day, check

8. (a) one person; (b) assets; (c) insured, bonded; (d) custody; (e) divided, duplication; (f) should be used (g) reviews

9. (a) departments and individuals; (b) verification, approval, and recording; (c) properly verified and approved

10. purchase requisition

11. purchase order

12. receiving report

Part III

CASH DISBURSEMENTS JOURNAL

DATE		CH. NO.	PAYEE	ACCOUNT DEBITED	P.R.	OTHER ACCOUNTS DEBIT		CASH CREDIT	
19—									
Nov.	5	23	Lon Dial, Petty Cashier	Petty Cash		50	00	50	00

CASH DISBURSEMENTS JOURNAL

DATE		CH. NO.	PAYEE	ACCOUNT DEBITED	P.R.	OTHER ACCOUNTS DEBIT		CASH CREDIT	
19—									
Nov.	25	97	Lon Dial, Petty Cashier	Transportation-in		22	75		
				Misc. Gen. Exp.		13	25		
				Office Supplies		3	50		
				Delivery Expense		8	00	47	50

Part IV

1. Book balance of cash ....   Bank statement balance ....

       Add: (f)   Add: (d)

       Deduct: (a) (c) (e)   Deduct: (b) (g)

2. (f) (a) (c) (e)

Part V

May	8	Purchases	3,675.00	
		Transportation-in	125.00	
		Accounts Payable—Vee Company		3,800.00
	26	Discounts Lost	75.00	
		Accounts Payable—Vee Company		75.00
July	5	Accounts Payable—Vee Company	3,875.00	
		Cash		3,875.00

Part VI

DATE		PAYEE	VCHR. NO.	CH. NO.	VOUCHERS PAYABLE DR.	PURCHASES DISCOUNT CR.	CASH CR.
Feb.	1	Union Truck Company	2	1	60 00		60 00
	8	Inter-City Wholesale Company	1	2	2 000 00	40 00	1 960 00
	13	Alpha Supply Company	3	3	250 00		250 00
	15	Payroll	5	4	1 000 00		1 000 00
	17	Treadwell and Son	4	5	700 00	14 00	686 00
	18	Morning Gazette	6	6	75 00		75 00
	21	WSID Radio Station	8	7	175 00		175 00
	26	Dale Brothers	7	8	1 250 00	25 00	1 225 00
	28	Neal Realty Company	11	9	500 00		500 00
	28	Payroll	12	10	1 000 00		1 000 00
					7 010 00	79 00	6 931 00

VOUCHER REGISTER

	DATE		VCHR. NO.	PAYEE	WHEN AND HOW PAID			VOUCHERS PAYABLE CREDIT		PURCHASES DEBIT		TRANS-PORTA-TION–IN DEBIT		
					DATE		CH. NO.							
1	Feb.	1	1	Inter-City Wholesale Co.	Feb.	8	2	2,000	00	2,000	00			1
2		1	2	Union Truck Company		1	1	60	00			60	00	2
3		5	3	Alpha Supply Company		13	3	250	00					3
4		9	4	Treadwell and Son		17	5	700	00	675	00	25	00	4
5		15	5	Payroll		15	4	1,000	00					5
6		18	6	Morning Gazette		18	6	75	00					6
7		18	7	Dale Brothers		26	8	1,250	00	1,250	00			7
8		21	8	WSID Radio Station		21	7	175	00					8
9		24	9	Office Sales Co.				500	00					9
10		25	10	Radion Company				1,875	00	1,875	00			10
11		28	11	Neal Realty Company		28	9	500	00					11
12		28	12	Payroll		28	10	1,000	00					12
13		28		Totals				9,385	00	5,800	00	85	00	13

VOUCHER REGISTER

	SALES SALARIES EXPENSE DEBIT		ADVER-TISING EXPENSE DEBIT		OFFICE SALARIES EXPENSE DEBIT		OTHER ACCOUNTS DEBIT				
							ACCOUNT NAME	P.R.	AMOUNT		
1											1
2											2
3							Store Supplies		250	00	3
4											4
5	625	00			375	00					5
6			75	00							6
7											7
8			175	00							8
9							Office Equipment		500	00	9
10											10
11							Rent Expense		500	00	11
12	625	00			375	00					12
13	1,250	00	250	00	750	00			1,250	00	13

GENERAL LEDGER

Cash

Date	Debit	Credit	Balance
Feb. 28		6,931.00	6,931.00

Transportation-in

Date	Debit	Credit	Balance
Feb. 28	85.00		85.00

Store Supplies

Date	Debit	Credit	Balance
Feb. 5	250.00		250.00

Rent Expense

Date	Debit	Credit	Balance
Feb. 28	500.00		500.00

Office Equipment

Date	Debit	Credit	Balance
Feb. 24	500.00		500.00

Sales Salaries Expense

Date	Debit	Credit	Balance
Feb. 28	1,250.00		1,250.00

Vouchers Payable

Date	Debit	Credit	Balance
Feb. 28		9,385.00	9,385.00
28	7,010.00		2,375.00

Advertising Expense

Date	Debit	Credit	Balance
Feb. 28	250.00		250.00

Purchases

Date	Debit	Credit	Balance
Feb. 28	5,800.00		5,800.00

Office Salaries Expense

Date	Debit	Credit	Balance
Feb. 28	750.00		750.00

Purchases Discounts

Date	Debit	Credit	Balance
Feb. 28		79.00	79.00

NERO SALES COMPANY
Schedule of Vouchers Payable
February 28, 19—

Voucher Number	Payee	Amount
9	Office Sales Company	$ 500
10	Radion Company	1,875
	Total Vouchers Payable	$2,375

8

Credit Sales and Receivables

Your objectives in studying this chapter should include learning how to:

Prepare entries to account for credit card sales.

Prepare entries accounting for bad debts both by the allowance method and the direct write-off method.

Explain the materiality principle and the full-disclosure principle.

Calculate the interest on promissory notes and the discount on notes receivable discounted.

Prepare entries to record the receipt of promissory notes and their payment or dishonor.

Prepare entries to record the discounting of notes receivable, and if dishonored, their dishonor.

Prepare reversing entries and explain the reasons for their use.

Define or explain the words and phrases listed in the chapter Glossary.

Topical Outline

I. Credit card sales

    A. Receipts from some credit card sales are deposited like checks into a business's bank account for immediate cash credit.

    B. Receipts from other credit card sales are sent to the credit card company for payment. The business has an account receivable from the credit card company until payment is received.

II. Bad debts—accounts of customers who do not pay

    A. A necessary expense associated with selling on credit.

    B. Bad debt expense should be matched with the sales that resulted in the bad debts.

    C. Methods of accounting for bad debts

        1. Allowance method—estimate made at end of each accounting period of total bad debts expected from sales. (This method is designed to satisfy the requirements of the matching principle.)

        2. Direct write-off method—uncollectible accounts written off directly to Bad Debts Expense. (This method mismatches revenues and expenses.)

    D. Methods of estimating bad debt expense

        1. Income statement approach—bad debt expense is calculated as a percentage of credit sales.

        2. Balance sheet approach—desired credit balance in Allowance for Doubtful Accounts is calculated:

            a. As a percentage of outstanding receivables (simplified approach).

            b. By aging of accounts receivable.

    E. Recovery of bad debts

        1. Reinstate customer's account (reverse original write-off).

        2. Record collection of reinstated account.

III. Installment accounts and notes receivable

    A. Installment account receivable—an account receivable which permits a customer to make periodic payments over several months and which usually earns interest.

    B. Note receivable—a written document promising payment and signed by the customer.

        1. Promissory notes are notes payable to the maker of the note and notes receivable to the payee.

        2. Notes receivable generally preferred by creditors over accounts receivable.

    C. Calculating interest

$$\text{Principal of note} \times \text{Annual rate of interest} \times \text{Time of note expressed in years} = \text{Interest}$$

    D. Accounting for notes receivable

        1. Record receipt of note.

        2. Record end-of-period adjustment for accrued interest.

        3. Record receipt of payment on note.

        4. If note dishonored, amount of note should be removed from Notes Receivable account and charged back to the account of maker.

        5. Reversing entries—not required; a technique that enables a bookkeeper to forget an accrued item once its adjusting entry has been entered.

E. Discounting notes receivable—owner endorses and delivers note to the bank for cash.

   1. Discount period—the time the bank holds the note.
   2. Bank discount—the amount of interest the bank charges during the discount period.
   3. Proceeds of the note—the maturity value of the note minus the bank discount.
   4. Contingent liability—usually the person who discounts the note is liable for payment of the note if it is dishonored by maker.

IV. Accounting principles

   A. Materiality principle—strict adherence to any accounting principle is not required if lack of adherence will not produce an error sufficiently large as to influence the judgment of financial statement readers.
   B. Full disclosure principle—financial statements and their accompanying notes must disclose all information of a material nature relating to the financial position and operating results of the company for which they are prepared.

Part I

Many of the important ideas and concepts discussed in Chapter 8 are reflected in the following list of key terms. Test your understanding of these terms by matching the appropriate definitions with the terms. Record the number identifying the most appropriate definition in the blank space next to each term.

23	Aging accounts receivable	16	Installment accounts receivable
19	Allowance for doubtful accounts	2	Maker of a note
5	Allowance method of accounting for bad debts	13	Materiality principle
3	Bad debt	21	Maturity date of a note
14	Bank discount	11	Maturity value of a note
7	Contingent liability	8	Notes receivable discounted
10	Direct write-off method of accounting for bad debts	20	Notice of protest
22	Discount period of a note	18	Payee of a note
1	Discounting a note receivable	6	Proceeds of a discounted note
12	Dishonoring a note	9	Protest fee
4	Full-disclosure principle	17	Realizable value
		15	Reversing entry

1. Selling a note receivable to a bank or other concern.

2. One who signs a note and promises to pay it at maturity.

3. An uncollectible account receivable.

4. The accounting requirement that financial statements and their accompanying notes disclose all information of a material nature relating to the financial position and operating results of the company for which they were prepared.

5. An accounting procedure that (1) estimates the bad debts arising from credit sales and reports bad debt expense during the period of the sales, and (2) reports accounts receivable in the balance sheet net of estimated uncollectibles which is their estimated realizable value.

6. The maturity value of a note minus any interest deducted because of its being discounted before maturity.

7. A potential liability that will become an actual liability if and only if certain events occur.

8. Notes receivable that have been discounted or sold by the payee and for which the payee is contingently liable.

9. The fee charged for preparing and issuing a notice of protest.

10. The accounting procedure whereby uncollectible accounts are not estimated in advance and are not charged to expense until they prove to be uncollectible.

11. Principal of the note plus any interest due on the note's maturity date.

12. Refusal of a promissory note's maker to pay the amount due upon maturity of the note.

13. The accounting rule that strict adherence to any accounting principle is not required if lack of adherence will not produce an error sufficiently large as to influence the judgment of financial statement readers.

14. The amount of interest charged by a bank when the interest is deducted in advance from money loaned.

15. An entry, made as a bookkeeping convenience at the beginning of an accounting period, the debit and credit of which are opposite to an adjusting entry for an accrual that was made at the end of the previous period. As a result of this entry, the subsequent receipt or payment of cash can be debited (or credited) entirely to the expense (or revenue) account.

16. Accounts receivable that allow the customer to make periodic payments over several months and which typically earn interest.

17. The amount of cash that should be received from the conversion of an asset into cash in the ordinary course of business.

18. The one to whom a promissory note is made payable.

19. The estimated amount of accounts receivable that will prove uncollectible.

20. A document informing each endorser of a promissory note that the note was presented for payment on its due date and payment was refused.

21. The date on which a note and any interest are due and payable.

22. The number of days following the date on which a note is discounted at the bank until the maturity date of the note.

23. A process of classifying accounts receivable in terms of how long they have been outstanding.

Part II

On December 12 Lark Company received from Guy Hall, a customer, $300 in cash and a $1,500, 12%, 60-day note dated December 11 in granting a time extension on Hall's past-due account. On December 31 Lark Company recorded the accrued interest on the note and Guy Hall paid the note and its interest on the following February 9. Complete the general journal entries to record these transactions.

DATE		ACCOUNT TITLES AND EXPLANATION	P.R.	DEBIT	CREDIT
Dec.	12	Cash		300	
		Note Receivable		1500	
		Accts Rec. - Guy Hall			1800
		Received cash and a note in granting a time			
		extension on a past-due account.			
	31	Interest Receivable		10	
		Interest Earned			10
		To record accrued interest on a note receivable.			
Feb.	9	Cash		1530	
		Note Receivable - G Hall			1500
		Interest Receivable			10
		Interest Earned			20
		Received payment of a note and interest.			

112

Part III

On March 1 Lark Company accepted a $1,200, 12%, 60-day note dated that day from a customer, Mary Dale, in granting a time extension on the customer's past due account. When Lark Company presented the note for payment on April 30, it was dishonored, and on December 20 Lark Company wrote off the debt as uncollectible. Complete the following entries to record the dishonor and the write-off against the company's Allowance for Doubtful Accounts.

DATE		ACCOUNT TITLES AND EXPLANATION	P.R.	DEBIT	CREDIT
Apr.	30	Acct Rec - M. Dale		1224	
		Note Recievable			1200
		Interest Earned			24
		To charge the account of Mary Dale for her			
		dishonored $1,200, 12%, 60-day note.			
Dec.	20	Allowance for Doubtful Accts		1224	
		Acct Rec-M.Dale -Bad debt			1224
		To write off the uncollectible note of Mary Dale.			

Part IV

On April 2 Lark Company received from Sam Fox, a customer, a $1,000, 12%, 60-day note dated that day in granting a time extension on the customer's past-due account. Lark Company held the note until April 26 and then discounted it at its bank at 14%. The note was not protested at maturity. Complete the following entries for this note.

DATE		ACCOUNT TITLES AND EXPLANATION	P.R.	DEBIT	CREDIT
Apr.	2	Note Rec. - S. Fox		1000	
		Acct Rec - SFox			1000
		Received a note in granting a time extension on			
		a past-due account.			
	26	Cash		1005 72	
		Note Rec.			1000
		Int earned			5 72
		Discounted the Sam Fox note at 14%.			

1020
1020- 360 = 14.28
————
1005.72

113

Part V

On June 10 Lark Company received a $2,000, 12%, 60-day note dated that day from Ted Sack, a customer, in granting a time extension on his past-due account. The company held the note until June 16 and then discounted it at its bank at 14%. On August 10 Lark Company received notice protesting the note. It paid the bank the maturity value of the note plus a $5 protest fee. On October 9 Lark Company received a $2,085.90 check from Ted Sack in payment of the maturity value of his dishonored note, the protest fee, and interest on both for 60 days beyond maturity. Complete the following general journal entries to record this series of transactions.

DATE		ACCOUNT TITLES AND EXPLANATION	P.R.	DEBIT	CREDIT
June	10	Note Rec – T. Sack		2000	
		Acct Rec			2000
		Received a note in granting a time extension on			
		a past-due account.			
June	16	Cash		1997 16	
		Int. Exp		2 84	
		Note Rec			2000
		Discounted the Ted Sack note at 14%.			
Aug.	10	Acct Rec – T. Sack		2045	
		Cash			2045
		Paid the bank the maturity value of the Ted Sack			
		note plus a protest fee.			
Oct.	9	Cash		2085 90	
		Acct Rec – T. Sack			2045
		Int. Earned			40 90
		Received payment of the maturity value of the			
		Ted Sack note plus the protest fee and interest			
		on both for 60 days beyond maturity.			

Mat. = 2040

14% – 54d = $\frac{42.84}{1997.16}$ 285.60

114

Part VI

Marin Company uses the allowance method in accounting for bad debt losses, and over the past several years it has experienced an average loss equal to one fourth of 1% of its credit sales. During 198A the company sold $928,000 of merchandise on credit, including a $98 credit sale to Gus Bell on March 5, 198A. The $98 had not been paid by the year's end.

1. If at the end of 198A Marin Company, in providing for estimated bad debt losses, assumes history will repeat, it will provide an allowance for 198A estimated bad debts equal to _____.25_____% of its $928,000 of 198A charge sales; and the adjusting entry to record the allowance will appear as follows: (Complete the following entry.)

DATE		ACCOUNT TITLES AND EXPLANATION	P.R.	DEBIT	CREDIT
198A					
Dec.	31	Bad debt expense		2320	
		Allowance for doubtful accts			2320
		To record estimated bad debts.			

2. The debit of the foregoing entry is to the expense account, ___Bad debt___ _____, which is closed to the ___Income Summary___ account at the end of the accounting period, just as any other expense account is closed.

3. The effect of the foregoing adjusting entry on the 198A income statement of Marin Company is to cause an estimated amount of bad debts expense to be deducted from the $928,000 of revenue from 198A charge sales. This complies with the accounting principle of _____ ___matching revenues & expenses___ _____.

4. The credit of the foregoing adjusting entry is to the contra account ___Allowance___ ___for doubtful accts,___ _____. On the December 31, 198A, balance sheet the balance of this contra account is subtracted from the balance of the ___Accts Rec___ account to show the amount that is expected to be realized from the accounts receivable.

5. On March 31, 198B, the Accounts Receivable controlling account and the Allowance for Doubtful Accounts account of Marin Company had the following balances:

Accounts Receivable		Allowance for Doubtful Accounts	
Mar. 31 65,625	Aprl 8B 98	Aprl, 8B 98	Mar. 31 4,475

A balance sheet which was prepared on March 31, 198B, would show that Marin Company expects to collect $ ___61,150___ of its accounts receivable.

6. On April 1, 198B, Marin Company decided the $98 account of Gus Bell (sale made on March 5 of the previous year) was uncollectible and wrote it off as a bad debt with the following entry: (Complete the entry and post to the above T-accounts the portions affecting the accounts.)

DATE		ACCOUNT TITLES AND EXPLANATION	P.R.	DEBIT	CREDIT
198B					
Apr.	1	Allow. for Doubtful Accts		98	
		Acct Rec - Gus Bell			98
		To write off the account of Gus Bell.			

7. If a balance sheet was prepared immediately after the entry writing off the uncollectible account of Gus Bell was posted, it would show that Marin Company expected to collect $ _____61,150_____ of its accounts receivable. Consequently, the write-off _____ (did, did not) affect the net balance sheet amount of accounts receivable. Likewise, the entry writing off the account did not record the loss as an expense because the loss and expense were anticipated and recorded in the _____adjusting_____ entry made on December 31, 198A, the year of the sale.

Part VII

Pell Company sells almost exclusively for cash, but it does make a few small charge sales, and it also occasionally has a small bad debt loss which it accounts for by the direct write-off method.

1. Give below the entry made by Pell Company on February 5 to write off the $55 uncollectible account of Joan Bond (goods sold during previous period).

DATE		ACCOUNT TITLES AND EXPLANATION	P.R.	DEBIT	CREDIT
Feb.	5	Bad debt Exp		55	
		Acct Rec - J.Bond			55

2. Writing off the foregoing bad debt directly to the Bad Debts Expense account violates the accounting principle of _____matching revenues & expenses_____. However, due to the accounting principle of _____materiality_____ the direct write-off is permissible in this case because the company's bad debt losses are immaterial in relation to its sales.

Part VIII

A company that ages its accounts receivable and increases its allowance for doubtful accounts to an amount sufficient to provide for estimated bad debts had a $75 debit balance in its Allowance for Doubtful Accounts account on December 31. If on that date it estimated that $1,800 of its accounts receivable were uncollectible, it should make a year-end adjusting entry crediting $ _____1875_____ to its Allowance for Doubtful Accounts account.

Part IX

Pierce Company allows its customers to use two credit cards: the University National Bank credit card and the Community Credit Card. Using the information given below, prepare general journal entries for Pierce Company to record the following credit card transactions:

a) University National Bank charges a 3% service fee for sales on its credit card. As a commercial customer of the bank, Pierce Company receives immediate credit when it makes its daily deposit of sales receipts.

    May 2 Sold merchandise for $525 to customers who used the University National Bank credit card.

MAY 2	Cash		509 25		
	Credit Card Expenses		15 75		
	Sales				525

b) Community Credit Card Company charges 4% of sales for use of its card. Pierce Company submits accumulated sales receipts to Community Company and is paid within seven to ten days.

    May 3 Sold merchandise for $675 to customers using the Community Credit Card. Submitted receipts to Community Company for payment.

    May 14 Received amount due from Community Credit Card Company.

MAY 3	Acct Rec		675		
	Sales				675
14	Cash		648		
	Credit Card Expenses		27		
	Acct Rec				675

Solutions for Chapter 8

Part I

Part II

Dec. 12	Cash	300.00	
	Notes Receivable	1,500.00	
	Accounts Receivable—Guy Hall		1,800.00
31	Interest Receivable	10.00	
	Interest Earned		10.00
Feb. 9	Cash	1,530.00	
	Interest Receivable		10.00
	Interest Earned		20.00
	Notes Receivable		1,500.00

Part III

Apr. 30	Accounts Receivable—Mary Dale	1,224.00	
	Interest Earned		24.00
	Notes Receivable		1,200.00
Dec. 20	Allowance for Doubtful Accounts	1,224.00	
	Accounts Receivable—Mary Dale		1,224.00

Part IV

Apr. 2	Notes Receivable	1,000.00	
	Accounts Receivable—Sam Fox		1,000.00
26	Cash	1,005.72	
	Interest Earned		5.72
	Notes Receivable		1,000.00

Part V

June 10	Notes Receivable	....	2,000.00	
	Accounts Receivable—Ted Sack	....		2,000.00
16	Cash	....	1,997.16	
	Interest Expense	....	2.84	
	Notes Receivable	....		2,000.00
Aug. 10	Accounts Receivable—Ted Sack	....	2,045.00	
	Cash	....		2,045.00
Oct. 9	Cash	....	2,085.90	
	Interest Earned	....		40.90
	Accounts Receivable—Ted Sack	....		2,045.00

Part VI

1. one fourth of 1

Dec. 31	Bad Debts Expense	....	2,320.00	
	Allowance for Doubtful Accounts	....		2,320.00

2. Bad Debts Expense, Income Summary
3. matching revenues and expenses
4. Allowance for Doubtful Accounts, Accounts Receivable
5. $61,150

6.	Apr. 1	Allowance for Doubtful Accounts	....	98.00	
		Accounts Receivable—Gus Bell	....		98.00

7. $61,150, did not, adjusting

Part VII

1.	Feb. 5	Bad Debts Expense	....	55.00	
		Accounts Receivable—Joan Bond	....		55.00

2. matching revenues and expenses, materiality

Part VIII

$1,875

Part IX

a)	May 2	Cash	....	509.25	
		Credit Card Expense	....	15.75	
		Sales	....		525.00
b)	May 3	Accounts Receivable—Community Company	....	675.00	
		Sales	....		675.00
	14	Cash	....	648.00	
		Credit Card Expense	....	27.00	
		Accounts Receivable—Community Company	....		675.00

9

Inventories and Cost of Goods Sold

Your objectives in studying this chapter should include learning how to:

Calculate the cost of an inventory based on (a) specific invoice prices, (b) weighted-average cost, (c) FIFO, and (d) LIFO.

Explain the income tax effect of the use of LIFO.

Describe the requirements of the consistency principle.

Describe the requirements of the conservatism principle.

Calculate the lower of cost or market amount of an inventory.

Explain the effect of an inventory error on the income statements of the current and succeeding years.

Prepare entries to record merchandise transactions under a perpetual inventory system.

Estimate an inventory by the retail method and by the gross profit method.

Define or explain the words and phrases listed in the chapter Glossary.

Topical Outline

I. Inventory accounting

  A. Merchandise inventory

    1. The tangible property a merchandising business holds for sale.
    2. Usually the largest current asset of a merchandising concern.

  B. Major objective in inventory accounting

    1. The proper determination of income through the process of matching appropriate costs against revenues.
    2. Means assigning costs of inventory for sale during the accounting period either to cost of goods sold or to ending inventory.

II. Periodic inventory system

  A. Cost of ending inventory is determined by:

    1. Determining quantity of each item on hand.
    2. Assigning a cost to the quantities on hand.

  B. Cost of goods sold is calculated by subtracting cost of ending inventory from goods available for sale.

  C. Four ways to assign costs

    1. Specific invoice prices

      a. Each inventory item is matched with its invoice price.
      b. This method is of practical use only with relatively high-priced items of which only a few are sold.

    2. Weighted-average cost

      a. Total cost of beginning inventory and purchases is divided by number of units to find average cost.
      b. This method tends to smooth out price fluctuations.

    3. First-in, first-out (FIFO)

      a. Costs are assigned under the assumption that the oldest goods are sold first. (This pricing method may be assumed even if physical flow of goods does not follow this pattern.)
      b. With FIFO method, inventory on the balance sheet most closely approximates current replacement cost.

    4. Last-in, first-out (LIFO)

      a. Costs are assigned under the assumption that the most recent purchases are sold first.
      b. Use of LIFO method results in better matching of current costs and revenues.
      c. LIFO offers a tax advantage for users during a period of rising prices.

  D. Items included on an inventory

    1. All goods owned by the business and held for sale regardless of the physical location of the goods.
    2. All costs incurred in bringing an article to its existing condition and location.

III. Lower of cost or market

  A. Inventory is normally reported on the balance sheet at market value whenever market is lower than cost.

    1. Market normally means replacement cost.
    2. Merchandise is written down to market because the value of the merchandise to the company has declined.

B. Lower of cost or market pricing is applied either:

   1. To the inventory as a whole, or
   2. Separately to each product in the inventory.

C. Exceptions

   1. Inventory should never be valued at more than its net realizable value (expected sales price less additional costs to sell).
   2. Inventory should never be valued at less than net realizable value minus a normal profit margin.

IV. Accounting principles

  A. Principle of consistency

     1. Requires a persistent application of an accounting method, period after period.

  B. Full-disclosure principle

     1. Requires a full disclosure of the nature of any change in accounting methods.

  C. Principle of conservatism

     1. When two estimates of amounts to be received or paid in the future are about equally likely, the less optimistic estimate should be used.
     2. Inventory cannot be written up to market when market exceeds cost.

  D. Principle of materiality

     1. In pricing an inventory, incidental costs of acquiring merchandise may be treated as expenses of the period in which incurred.

V. Inventory errors

  A. Periodic inventory system

     1. An error in determining the end-of-period inventory will cause misstatements in cost of goods sold, gross profit, net income, current assets, and owners' equity.
     2. Error will carry forward in succeeding period's cost of goods sold, gross profit, and net income.
     3. Errors in cost of goods sold and net income will be offset by errors in the following period.

VI. Perpetual inventory system

  A. Updates the Merchandise Inventory account after each purchase and each sale.
  B. Does not use a Purchases account; cost of items purchased debited directly to Merchandise Inventory.
  C. Requires two entries to record a sale of merchandise.
  D. Merchandise Inventory account serves as a controlling account to a subsidiary Merchandise Inventory Ledger, which contains a separate record for each product in stock.
  E. Using LIFO a perpetual inventory system results in different amounts of cost of goods sold and ending inventory than under a periodic inventory system.

VII. Estimated inventories

  A. Retail inventory method

     1. Used to estimate ending inventory on the ratios of cost of goods for sale at cost and cost of goods for sale at retail.
     2. Satisfactory for interim statements, but a physical inventory should be taken at least once a year.

  B. Gross profit method

     1. Similar to retail method, but does not require information about retail price of beginning inventory, purchases, and markups.
     2. Company must know its normal gross profit margin or rate.

Part I

Many of the important ideas and concepts discussed in Chapter 9 are reflected in the following list of key terms. Test your understanding of these terms by matching the appropriate definitions with the terms. Record the number identifying the most appropriate definition in the blank space next to each term.

_____	Conservatism principle	_____	Markdown
_____	Consignee	_____	Markon
_____	Consignor	_____	Markup
_____	Consistency principle	_____	Net realizable value
_____	FIFO inventory pricing	_____	Normal markup
_____	Gross profit inventory method	_____	Periodic inventory system
_____	Interim statements	_____	Perpetual inventory system
_____	Inventory cost ratio	_____	Retail inventory method
_____	Inventory ticket	_____	Specific invoice inventory pricing
_____	LIFO inventory pricing	_____	Weighted-average cost inventory pricing
_____	Lower-of-cost-or-market pricing		

1. The expected sales price of inventory items less additional costs to sell.

2. The pricing of an inventory under the assumption that the first items received were the first items sold.

3. An accounting method whereby inventory is reported in the financial statements at the lower of what the inventory actually cost or market value, which normally is what it would cost to replace the inventory on the balance sheet date.

4. A phrase meaning the same as markon.

5. The accounting rule requiring a persistent application of a selected accounting method or procedure, period after period.

6. An increase in the sales price of inventory above the normal markon given to an item.

7. The ratio of goods available for sale at cost to goods available for sale at retail prices.

8. An owner of goods who ships them to another party who will then sell the goods for the owner.

9. A procedure for estimating an ending inventory in which an estimated cost of goods sold based on past gross profit rates is subtracted from the cost of goods available for sale to arrive at an estimated ending inventory.

10. The pricing of an inventory where each inventory item can be associated with a specific invoice and be priced accordingly.

11. A form attached to the counted items in the process of taking a physical inventory.

12. An inventory pricing system in which the units in the beginning inventory of a product and in each purchase of the product are weighted by the number of units in the beginning inventory and in each purchase to determine a weighted-average cost per unit of the product, and after which this weighted-average cost is used to price the ending inventory of the product.

13. The pricing of an inventory under the assumption that the last items received were the first items sold.

14. A reduction in the marked selling price of an item.

15. The accounting principle that guides accountants to select the less optimistic estimate when two estimates of amounts to be received or paid are about equally likely.

16. An inventory system in which the Merchandise Inventory account is updated only once each accounting period, based on a physical count of the inventory.

17. An inventory system in which cost of goods sold is recorded after each sale and the Merchandise Inventory account is updated after each purchase and each sale.

18. A method for estimating an ending inventory based on the ratio of the cost of goods for sale at cost and cost of goods for sale at marked selling prices.

19. One who receives and holds goods owned by another party for the purpose of selling the goods for the owner.

20. Monthly or quarterly financial statements prepared in between the regular year-end statements.

21. The normal amount or percentage of cost that is added to the cost of an item to arrive at its selling price.

Part II

Complete the following by filling in the blanks.

1. Consistency in the use of an inventory costing method is particularly important if there is to

   be _____

   _____.

2. In a perpetual inventory system a running record is maintained for each inventory item of the number of units received as units are received, the number of units sold as units are sold,

   and after each receipt or sale, the number of _____

   _____.

3. When a company changes its accounting procedures, the _____

   principle requires that the nature of the change, justification for the change, and the effect of

   the change on _____ be disclosed in the notes
   accompanying the financial statements.

4. Two exceptions to the idea that market means replacement cost are:

   a. _____

   _____.

   b. _____

   _____.

5. Inventories are generally priced at cost. However, a departure from cost may be necessary

   for _____

   _____

   _____.

126

6. An error in taking an end-of-period inventory will cause a misstatement of periodic net income for _____ (one, two) accounting periods because _____

_____

_____

_____.

7. When identical items are purchased during an accounting period at different costs, a problem arises as to which costs apply to the ending inventory and which apply to the goods sold. There are at least four commonly used ways of assigning costs to inventory and to goods sold. They are:

   a. _____;

   b. _____;

   c. _____;

   d. _____.

8. A major objective of accounting for inventories is the proper determination of periodic net income through the process of matching _____ and _____

_____. The matching process consists of determining how much of the cost of the goods that were for sale during an accounting period should be

deducted from the period's _____ and how much should be carried

forward as an asset, called _____,
to be matched against a future period's revenues.

9. Although changing back and forth from one inventory costing method to another might allow management to report the incomes it would prefer, the accounting principle of

_____ requires a company to use the same pricing method period after period unless it can justify the change.

10. Using _____ inventory pricing, a perpetual inventory system and a

periodic inventory system result in different amounts of _____

_____ and _____.

11. In the gross profit method of estimating an ending inventory, an average _____

_____ rate is used to determine esti-
mated cost of goods sold, and the ending inventory is then estimated by subtracting

estimated _____ from the
cost of goods for sale.

12. In separating cost of goods for sale into cost of goods sold and cost of goods unsold, the key

problem is that of assigning a cost to the _____

_____, but it should be observed that the procedures for assigning a cost to

the ending inventory are also the means of determining _____

_____ because whatever portion of the cost of goods available for sale is

assigned to ending inventory, the remainder goes to _____.

13. Cost of an inventory item includes _____

_____

_____

_____.

14. Use of the lower-of-cost-or-market rule places an inventory on the balance sheet at a
_____ figure. The argument in favor of this rule provides that
any loss should be _____ and taken in the year of the
_____.

15. When recording a sale of merchandise using a _____
(perpetual, periodic) inventory system, two journal entries must be made. One entry records
the revenue received for the sale and the second entry debits a(n) _____
_____ account.

Part III

A company had 600 units of Product Z in its end-of-year inventory. It began the year and had
purchased Product Z as follows:

Jan. 1	Inventory	200 units @ $0.50 =	$ 100
Mar. 15	Purchased	400 units @ 0.50 =	200
June 3	Purchased	300 units @ 0.60 =	180
Oct. 8	Purchased	600 units @ 0.70 =	420
Dec. 15	Purchased	500 units @ 0.80 =	400
		2,000	$1,300

In the spaces below show the portions of the $1,300 total cost of the foregoing 2,000 units that
should be assigned to the ending inventory and to the goods sold under the following
assumptions:

	Portions Assigned to—	
	Ending Inventory	Cost of Goods Sold
1. A first-in, first-out basis was used to price the ending inventory	$	$
2. A last-in, first-out basis was used to price the ending inventory	$	$
3. The ending inventory was priced on a weighted-average cost basis	$	$

128

Part IV

The following end-of-period information about a store's beginning inventory, purchases, markups, markdowns, and sales is available.

	At Cost	At Retail
Beginning inventory	$ 9,600	$12,000
Purchases, net	54,400	68,000
Transportation-in	1,680	
Additional markups		2,100
Markdowns		700
Sales		69,000

The above information is to be used to estimate the store's ending inventory by the retail method.

1. The store had goods for sale during the year calculated as follows:

	At Cost	At Retail
Beginning inventory	$ _____	$ _____
Purchases, net	_____	_____
Transportation-in	_____	_____
Additional markups	_____	_____
Goods for sale	_____	_____

2. The store's cost ratio was:

$ _____ / $ _____ = _____

3. Of the goods the store had for sale at market retail prices during the year, the following dollar amounts are gone because of—

Sales .... $ _____

And because of price markdowns, which in effect reduced the total goods for sale at retail ..... _____

    Total sales and markdowns .... $ _____

Which left the store an estimated ending inventory at retail (goods for sale at retail less sales and markdowns) .... $ _____

4. And when the store's cost ratio is applied to this estimated ending inventory at retail, the estimated ending inventory at cost is .... $ _____

Solutions for Chapter 9

Part I

Part II

1. comparability in the financial statements prepared period after period.

2. units remaining.

3. full-disclosure, net income

4. (a) market is never more than net realizable value, (b) market is never less than net realizable value minus a normal profit margin.

5. goods that have been damaged or have deteriorated and also when replacement costs for inventory items are less than the amounts paid for the items.

6. two, the ending inventory of one period becomes the beginning inventory of the next.

7. (a) specific invoice prices; (b) weighted average cost; (c) first-in, first-out; (d) last-in, first-out.

8. costs, revenues, revenues, merchandise inventory.

9. consistency

10. last-in, first-out; cost of goods sold; ending inventory.

11. gross profit, cost of goods sold

12. ending inventory, cost of goods sold, cost of goods sold.

13. the invoice price, less the discount, plus any additional incidental costs necessary to put the item in place and in condition for sale.

14. conservative, recognized, price decline

15. perpetual, cost of goods sold

Part III

	Portions Assigned to—	
	Ending Inventory	Cost of Goods Sold
1.	$470	$ 830
2.	300	1,000
3.	390	910

Part IV

	At Cost	At Retail
Goods for sale:		
Beginning inventory	$ 9,600	$12,000
Purchases, net	54,400	68,000
Transportation-in	1,680	
Additional markups		2,100
Goods for sale	$65,680	$82,100

Cost ratio: $65,680/$82,100 = .80

Sales at retail		$69,000
Markdowns		700
Total sales and markdowns .....~..............		$69,700
Ending inventory at retail		
($82,100 less $69,700)		$12,400
Ending inventory at cost ($12,400 × 80%)	$ 9,920	

10

Plant and Equipment

Your objectives in studying this chapter should include learning how to:

Tell what is included in the cost of a plant asset.

Allocate the cost of lump-sum purchases to the separate assets being purchased.

Describe the causes of depreciation and the reasons for depreciation accounting.

Calculate depreciation by the (a) straight-line, (b) units-of-production, (c) declining-balance, and (d) sum-of-the-years'-digits methods.

Explain how the accelerated cost recovery system defers income taxes.

Define or explain the words and phrases listed in the chapter Glossary.

Topical Outline

I. Plant and equipment

  A. Includes assets that are used in the production or sale of other assets and that have an expected service life longer than one accounting period.

  B. Cost of a plant asset

    1. Includes all normal and reasonable costs incurred in getting the asset into position and in condition for intended use.

    2. Must be allocated to the accounting periods that benefit from the asset's use.

    3. Must be allocated on a fair basis such as relative appraisal values, if two or more assets are purchased for one price.

  C. Service life of a plant asset—the period of time that it will be used in producing or selling other assets or services.

  D. Salvage value of a plant asset—the net amount that will be realized when the asset is disposed of at the end of its service life. The amount to be depreciated is the asset's cost minus its salvage value.

II. Depreciation

  A. The expiration of an asset's quantity of usefulness.

  B. The cost (less expected salvage value) of the asset must be allocated as an expense to the accounting periods benefited.

  C. Methods of allocating depreciation

    1. Straight-line—a method that allocates an equal share of the total estimated amount a plant asset will be depreciated during its service life to each accounting period in that life.

    2. Units-of-production—a method that allocates depreciation on a plant asset based on the relation of the units of product produced by the asset during a given period to the total units the asset is expected to produce during its entire life.

    3. Declining-balance—an accelerated depreciation method in which up to twice the straight-line rate of depreciation, without considering salvage value, is applied to the remaining book value of a plant asset to arrive at the asset's annual depreciation charge.

    4. Sum-of-the-years'-digits—an accelerated depreciation method that allocates depreciation to each year in a plant asset's life on a fractional basis. The denominator of the fractions used is the sum of the years' digits in the estimated service life of the asset, and the numerators are the years' digits in reverse order.

  D. For assets acquired or disposed of during a year, only a partial year's depreciation should be recorded.

  E. When accelerated depreciation is used and accounting periods do not coincide with the years in an asset's life, depreciation must be apportioned between periods if it is to be properly charged.

  F. Depreciation in the financial statements

    1. The cost of plant assets and their accumulated depreciation must be shown in the statements or in related footnotes.

    2. Depreciation method must be disclosed in a balance sheet footnote or other manner.

    3. Since depreciation is a process of allocating cost, the cost (net of depreciation) is not intended to represent value.

    4. Since depreciation expense is subtracted from revenues in arriving at net income, a company recovers the original cost of its depreciable assets through the sale of its products.

III. Accelerated depreciation for tax purposes

   A. Use of accelerated depreciation in preparing financial statements does not require that such methods also be used for tax purposes.

   B. Tax laws of the United States allow:

      1. Use of declining-balance or sum-of-the-years'-digits methods for certain assets purchased prior to 1981.

      2. For assets purchased after 1980, a new system of accelerated depreciation was adopted: the accelerated cost recovery system (ACRS).

         a. Depreciation rates under ACRS are specified in the law.

         b. A straight-line method may be used, but many taxpayers choose the ACRS method.

         c. ACRS depreciation generally is not acceptable for use in preparing financial statements.

IV. Control of plant assets

   A. Each plant asset should be separately identified.

   B. Periodic inventories should be taken to verify the existence and continued use of assets.

   C. Formal records of plant assets should be maintained.

      1. Controlling and subsidiary ledgers should be kept.

      2. Materiality principle may be applied for assets less than an established minimum cost.

Part I

Many of the important ideas and concepts discussed in Chapter 10 are reflected in the following list of key terms. Test your understanding of these terms by matching the appropriate definitions with the terms. Record the number identifying the most appropriate definition in the blank space next to each term.

_____ Accelerated cost recovery system (ACRS)

_____ Accelerated depreciation

_____ Book value

_____ Declining-balance depreciation

_____ Fixed asset

_____ Inadequacy

_____ Internal Revenue Code

_____ Land improvements

_____ Obsolescence

_____ Office Equipment Ledger

_____ Salvage value

_____ Service life

_____ Store Equipment Ledger

_____ Straight-line depreciation

_____ Sum-of-the-years'-digits depreciation

_____ Units-of-production depreciation

1. A plant asset.

2. The share of a plant asset's cost recovered at the end of its service life through a sale or as a trade-in allowance on a new asset.

3. A depreciation method that allocates depreciation on a plant asset based on the relation of the units of product produced by the asset during a given period to the total units the asset is expected to produce during its entire life.

4. The situation where because of new inventions and improvements, an old plant asset can no longer produce its product on a competitive basis.

5. Assets that improve or increase the value or usefulness of land but which have a limited useful life and are subject to depreciation.

6. A depreciation method in which up to twice the straight-line rate of depreciation, without considering salvage value, is applied to the remaining book value of a plant asset to arrive at the asset's annual depreciation charge.

7. A subsidiary ledger that contains a separate record for each item of office equipment owned.

8. A depreciation method that allocates an equal share of the total estimated amount a plant asset will be depreciated during its service life to each accounting period in that life.

9. The codification of the numerous tax laws passed by Congress.

10. A unique, accelerated depreciation method prescribed in the tax law for assets placed in service after 1980.

11. A depreciation method that allocates depreciation to each year in a plant asset's life on a fractional basis. The denominator of the fractions used is the sum of the years' digits in the estimated service life of the asset, and the numerators are the years' digits in reverse order.

12. The carrying amount for an item in the accounting records. When applied to a plant asset, it is the cost of the asset minus its accumulated depreciation.

13. Any depreciation method resulting in greater amounts of depreciation expense in the early years of a plant asset's life and lesser amounts in later years.

14. The period of time a plant asset is used in the production and sale of other assets or services.

15. A subsidiary ledger that contains a separate record for each item of store equipment owned.

16. The situation where a plant asset does not produce enough product to meet current needs.

137

Part II

Complete the following by filling in the blanks.

1. The estimated salvage value of a plant asset is the estimated portion of the asset's _____ that is expected to be recovered at the end of its service life.

2. There are several factors that affect the useful life of some assets. These factors include:

   a) _____;

   b) _____;

   c) _____.

3. To be classified as a plant asset, an asset must be _____
   _____;
   and it must have _____
   _____.

4. Amounts of accumulated depreciation shown on a balance sheet _____ (do, do not) represent funds accumulated to buy new assets when present assets wear out and must be discarded.

5. Recording depreciation _____ (is, is not) a process of recording the decline in the market value of a plant asset.

6. The tax advantage of accelerated depreciation is that _____
   _____.

7. Balance sheet amounts shown for plant assets may bear little relation to the market values of the plant assets because balance sheets show for plant assets _____
   _____ rather than market values.

8. If a company breaks even on its operations, it will eventually recover the cost of its plant assets through _____
   _____.

9. The cost of a plant asset includes _____
   _____
   _____.

10. Trucks held for sale by a dealer and land held for future expansion are not classified as plant assets because _____
    _____.

11. Recording depreciation _____ (is, is not) a process of recording the physical deterioration of a plant asset.

12. The book value of a plant asset is its "value" as shown by the books and consists of its cost minus its _____

    _____ .

13. Since a plant asset contributes to the production or sale of other assets for a period longer than one accounting period, if revenues and expenses are to be matched, the cost of the plant asset's quantity of usefulness must be _____

    _____

    _____ .

14. The amount of accumulated depreciation deducted on a balance sheet from a plant asset's cost represents that portion of the cost that has been charged off to _____

    _____ during the asset's life.

15. When a business buys a plant asset, it in effect buys a quantity of usefulness that will be consumed during the service life of the asset; and depreciation of the asset, as the phrase is used in accounting, is nothing more than an expiration of the asset's _____

    _____ _____ .

    Furthermore, recording depreciation on the asset is the process of _____

    _____

    _____

    _____ .

Part III

A machine was purchased for $7,000, terms 2/10, n/60, FOB vendor's factory. The invoice was paid within the discount period along with $175 of freight charges. The machine was installed on a special concrete base by the employees of the company that bought it. The concrete base and special power connections for the machine cost $575, and the wages of the employees during the period in which they installed the machine amounted to $425. The employees accidentally dropped the machine while moving it onto its special base, causing damages to the machine which cost $125 to repair. As a result of all this, the cost of the machine for accounting purposes

was $ _____ .

Part IV

A machine cost $8,000 and was estimated to have an eight-year service life and an $800 salvage value. It was further estimated that the machine would produce 40,000 units of product during its life. If the machine produced 9,000 units during its first year, the depreciation charge for the year was:

1. $ _____ calculated on a straight-line basis.

2. $ _____ calculated by the units-of-production method.

3. $ _____ calculated by the declining-balance method at twice the straight-line rate.

4. $ _____ calculated by the sum-of-the-years'-digits method.

139

Part V

In January 1986 a company purchased a light truck for $19,000. The truck is expected to last five years and have a salvage value of $1,000. For tax purposes, the truck is in the three-year class of assets, and the company is considering three depreciation alternatives: (a) straight line over five years, (b) straight line over three years, and (c) ACRS depreciation. Complete the table by showing the amount of depreciation to be taken each year under each of the three alternatives.

Depreciation Expense Each Year

	Straight line		
Year	Five-year (useful life)	Three-year option	ACRS
1986	_____	_____	_____
1987	_____	_____	_____
1988	_____	_____	_____
1989	_____	_____	_____
1990	_____	_____	_____
1991	_____	_____	_____

Part VI

A machine that cost $12,000 and upon which depreciation totaling $11,000 had been recorded was disposed of on January 1 of the current year. Give without explanation the general journal entries to record its disposal if the machine was sold for $1,000.

DATE	ACCOUNT TITLES AND EXPLANATION	P.R.	DEBIT	CREDIT

Solutions for Chapter 10

Part I

Part II

1. cost

2. a) wear and tear
    b) inadequacy
    c) obsolescence

3. used in the production or sale of other assets, a useful life longer than one accounting period

4. do not

5. is not

6. it defers the payment of income taxes

7. undepreciated costs

8. the sale of its product

9. all normal and reasonable expenditures necessary to get the asset in place and ready for use

10. they are not presently being used to produce or sell other assets

11. is not

12. accumulated depreciation

13. allocated to the several accounting periods during which it will be used

14. depreciation expense

15. quantity of usefulness, allocating the cost of the asset's quantity of usefulness to the accounting periods that will benefit from its use.

Part III

$8,013.

Part IV

1. $900   2. $1,620   3. $2,000   4. $1,600

Part V

Depreciation Expense Each Year

Straight line

Year	Five-year (useful life)	Three-year option	ACRS
1986	$1,900	$3,167	$4,750
1987	3,800	6,333	7,220
1988	3,800	6,333	7,030
1989	3,800	3,167	–0–
1990	3,800	–0–	–0–
1991	1,900	–0–	–0–

Part VI

Jan. 1	Cash	1,000.00	
	Accumulated Depreciation, Machinery	11,000.00	
	Machinery		12,000.00

11

Plant and Equipment; Intangible Assets

Your objectives in studying this chapter should include learning how to:

Prepare entries to record the purchase and sale or discarding of a plant asset.

Prepare entries to record the exchange of plant assets under accounting rules and under income tax rules and tell which rules should be applied in any given exchange.

Make the calculations and prepare the entries to account for revisions in depreciation rates.

Make the calculations and prepare the entries to account for plant asset repairs and betterments.

Prepare entries to account for wasting assets and for intangible assets.

Define or explain the words and phrases listed in the chapter Glossary.

Topical Outline

I. Disposal, sale, or exchange of a plant asset

    A. Discarding a plant asset

        1. Remove cost and accumulated depreciation from accounts.
        2. Record any remaining book value as a loss on disposal.
        3. If discarded asset is damaged, record any remaining book value not recovered through insurance as a loss.

    B. Selling a plant asset

        1. Remove cost and accumulated depreciation from accounts.
        2. If proceeds greater than book value, record a gain.
        3. If proceeds less than book value, record a loss.

    C. Exchanging plant assets

        1. For accounting purposes, a material book loss should be recognized in the accounts but a book gain should not.

            a. A book loss results when trade-in allowance is less than book value of traded asset.

                (1) If material, the loss must be recognized.
                (2) If not material, the loss may be charged to cost of new asset.

            b. A book gain results when trade-in allowance exceeds book value of asset.

            (New asset is taken into the accounts at an amount equal to the book value of the traded-in asset plus the cash given. This results in nonrecognition of the gain.)

        2. For tax purposes:

            a. Neither a gain nor a loss should be recognized at the time of the exchange; either a gain or a loss must be absorbed into the cost of the new asset.
            b. The cost basis of an asset acquired in an exchange is the sum of the book value of the old asset plus the cash given (it makes no difference whether there is a gain or a loss).

II. Revising depreciation rates

    A. Remaining cost to be depreciated is allocated over the remaining expected life (as revised).
    B. Depreciation expense of prior periods is not revised.

III. Ordinary and extraordinary repairs

    A. Ordinary repairs

        1. Repairs made to keep asset in normal good state of repair.
        2. Appear on income statement as expense.

    B. Extraordinary repairs

        1. Major repairs made to extend the service life beyond that originally estimated.
        2. Normally debited to the asset's Accumulated Depreciation account.

IV. Betterments

    A. Modification of an existing plant asset to make it more efficient, usually by replacing part of the asset with an improved or superior part.
    B. Debited to the asset account and depreciated over the remaining service life of the asset.

V. Capital and revenue expenditures

    A. Capital expenditures

        1. Costs charged to balance sheet accounts (debited to the asset or to Accumulated Depreciation) because the expenditure is expected to benefit future periods.

        2. Examples: betterments, extraordinary repairs.

    B. Revenue expenditures

        1. Charged to the income statement of the current period.

        2. Examples: ordinary repairs, rent, salaries.

VI. Natural resources

    A. Include wasting assets such as oil reserves, timber tracts, etc.

    B. As the resources are used, their cost should be allocated to expense, known as "depletion."

    C. The total amount of cost so allocated is reported as a credit to Accumulated Depletion.

VII. Intangible assets

    A. Have no physical existence.

    B. Represent certain legal rights and economic relationships beneficial to owner.

    C. Are amortized or written off to expense accounts over their estimated useful lives.

    D. Examples:

        1. Patents

        2. Copyrights

        3. Leaseholds (and leasehold improvements)

        4. Goodwill

        5. Trademarks and trade names

Part I

Many of the important ideas and concepts discussed in Chapter 11 are reflected in the following list of key terms. Test your understanding of these terms by matching the appropriate definitions with the terms. Record the number identifying the most appropriate definition in the blank space next to each term.

_____	Amortize	_____	Intangible asset
_____	Balance sheet expenditure	_____	Lease
_____	Betterment	_____	Leasehold
_____	Capital expenditure	_____	Leasehold improvements
_____	Copyright	_____	Lessee
_____	Depletion	_____	Lessor
_____	Extraordinary repairs	_____	Ordinary repairs
_____	Goodwill	_____	Patent
_____	Income tax rules	_____	Revenue expenditure

1. An exclusive right granted by the federal government to publish and sell a musical, literary, or art work for a period of years.

2. The amount a wasting asset is reduced through cutting, mining, or pumping.

3. The individual or enterprise that gives up possession of property under the terms of a lease contract.

4. An asset having no physical existence but having value due to the rights resulting from its ownership and possession.

5. Another name for capital expenditure.

6. To periodically write off as an expense a share of the cost of an asset, usually an intangible asset.

7. The rights granted to a lessee under the terms of a lease contract.

8. Repairs made to keep a plant asset in its normal good operating condition.

9. An exclusive right granted by the federal government to manufacture and sell a machine or mechanical device for a period of years.

10. Major repairs that extend the service life of a plant asset beyond the number of years originally estimated.

11. An expenditure that benefits only the current period because the value or asset obtained by the expenditure will fully expire before the end of the current accounting period.

12. The replacement of an existing asset portion with an improved or superior asset portion, the result of which is a more efficient or more productive asset.

13. An expenditure that benefits future periods because the value or asset obtained by the expenditure does not fully expire by the end of the current period.

14. That portion of the value of a business due to its expected ability to earn a rate of return greater than the average in its industry.

15. Improvements to leased property made by the lessee.

16. Rules governing how income for tax purposes and income taxes are to be calculated.

17. An individual or enterprise that is given possession of property under the terms of a lease contract.

18. A contract that grants the right to possess and use property.

Part II

Complete the following by filling in the blanks.

1. When a plant asset is taken into the accounts at its cost basis, this cost basis is used in recording _____ on the asset and any _____ on its sale.

2. In the final analysis, goodwill is always valued at the price at which _____ _____ _____ _____.

3. A gain or a loss on a plant asset exchange is not recognized in the accounts when the new asset is taken into the accounts at an amount equal to the _____ _____ of the traded-in asset plus the cash given in the exchange. This amount is called the _____ of the new asset.

4. The use of the income tax method in recording a plant asset exchange in which there is an immaterial loss is permissible under the accounting principle of _____ _____.

5. Federal income tax rules require that neither a gain nor a loss on a plant asset exchange be recognized for tax purposes and, therefore, differ from accounting principles in the treatment for _____ (gains, losses).

6. Intangible assets should be systematically amortized or written off to expense accounts over their estimated useful lives, which in no case should exceed _____ _____.

7. Two sets of depreciation records are avoided if the _____ _____ method is used in recording the exchange of like-purpose plant assets on which the loss is immaterial in amount. Under this method the new asset is taken into the accounts at its cost basis for tax purposes, which is equal to the sum of the book value of the traded-in asset plus the _____ given in the exchange.

8. In accounting, a business is said to have _____ when its earnings rate is greater than the earnings rate normally realized in its industry.

9. If a loss on an exchange of plant assets of like purpose is recorded as such, two sets of depreciation records must be kept throughout the life of the new asset, one for use in determining _____ for accounting purposes and another for determining _____ for tax purposes.

10. In recording plant asset exchanges, the APB ruled that a material _____ (gain, loss) should be recognized for accounting purposes but a _____ (gain, loss) should not be.

Part III

On January 8 a machine that cost $12,000 and on which $10,000 of depreciation had been recorded was traded in on a new machine of like purpose. The new machine could have been purchased without a trade-in for $14,000. Give without explanations the general journal entries to record the exchange under each of the following unrelated assumptions:

1. The old machine and $13,000 in cash were given for the new machine, and the loss was recognized in the accounts.

DATE	ACCOUNT TITLES AND EXPLANATION	P.R.	DEBIT	CREDIT

2. The old machine and $13,000 in cash were given for the new machine, and the income tax method was used to record the exchange.

DATE	ACCOUNT TITLES AND EXPLANATION	P.R.	DEBIT	CREDIT

3. The old machine and $10,500 in cash were given for the new machine.

DATE	ACCOUNT TITLES AND EXPLANATION	P.R.	DEBIT	CREDIT

Part IV

On March 1, 1986, a machine was installed in a factory at a $9,000 total cost. Straight-line depreciation was recorded on each December 31 of the machine's life under the assumption it would have no salvage value at the end of a 12-year life. On February 27, 1990, the machine was destroyed by fire. On March 4 the insurance company paid $4,500 in full settlement of the fire loss claim. In the space below, given the general journal entry to record the destruction of the machine and receipt of the $4,500 from the insurance company.

DATE	ACCOUNT TITLES AND EXPLANATION	P.R.	DEBIT	CREDIT

Part V

Ten years ago a machine was purchased and installed at a $12,000 cost. At that time it was estimated the machine would have a 12-year life and a $600 salvage value. At the beginning of the machine's 11th year the estimated number of years remaining in its useful life was changed from two to four years and its salvage value was changed from $600 to $700.

1. Straight-line depreciation at the rate of $ _____ per year was recorded on this machine during the first ten years of its life.

2. After depreciation for its tenth year was recorded, the book value of the machine was: Cost $ _____ minus $ _____ of accumulated depreciation equals a $ _____ book value.

3. And depreciation for each of the remaining four years in the machine's life should be calculated:

$$\frac{\text{Book Value} - \text{Salvage Value}}{\text{Remaining Useful Life}} = \text{Depreciation per Year}$$

$$\frac{\$\text{_____} - \text{_____}}{4 \text{ years}} = \$\text{_____ per Year}$$

Part VI

A machine that cost $15,500 was depreciated using straight line under the assumption that it would have a six-year life and a $1,100 salvage value. At the beginning of its sixth year the machine received a major overhaul that cost $4,200 and extended its life for two years beyond the six originally estimated. The overhaul did not change the machine's estimated salvage value nor increase its efficiency.

1. Give without an explanation the entry to record the overhaul.

DATE	ACCOUNT TITLES AND EXPLANATION	P.R.	DEBIT	CREDIT

2. Give the entry to record the sixth year's depreciation on the machine.

DATE	ACCOUNT TITLES AND EXPLANATION	P.R.	DEBIT	CREDIT

Part VII

A machine that cost $25,000 was depreciated using straight line under the assumption it would have a ten-year life and no salvage value. After four years of use, new automatic controls (not available when the machine was first purchased) that cost $7,500 and reduced operating labor by 50% were placed on the machine. The addition of the controls did not affect the machine's estimated life nor its zero salvage value.

1. Give without an explanation the entry to record the addition of the new controls.

DATE	ACCOUNT TITLES AND EXPLANATION	P.R.	DEBIT	CREDIT

2. Give the entry to record the fifth year's depreciation on the machine.

DATE	ACCOUNT TITLES AND EXPLANATION	P.R.	DEBIT	CREDIT

Part I

Part II

1. depreciation, loss or gain
2. a seller is willing to accept and a buyer is willing to buy
3. book value, cost basis
4. materiality
5. losses
6. 40 years
7. income tax, cash
8. goodwill
9. net income, depreciation expense
10. loss, gain

Part III

1. Jan. 8 Machinery 14,000.00
   Loss on Exchange of Machinery 1,000.00
   Accumulated Depreciation, Machinery 10,000.00
      Machinery 12,000.00
      Cash 13,000.00

2. Jan. 8 Machinery 15,000.00
   Accumulated Depreciation, Machinery 10,000.00
      Machinery 12,000.00
      Cash 13,000.00

3. Jan. 8 Machinery 12,500.00
   Accumulated Depreciation, Machinery 10,000.00
      Machinery 12,000.00
      Cash 10,500.00

Part IV

Mar. 4	Cash	4,500.00	
	Loss from Fire	1,500.00	
	Accumulated Depreciation, Machinery	3,000.00	
	Machinery		9,000.00

Part V

1. $950

2. Cost $12,000 minus $9,500 of accumulated depreciation equals a $2,500 book value.

3. $$\frac{\$2,500 - \$700}{4 \text{ years}} = \$450 \text{ per year}$$

Part VI

1.	Jan. 9	Accumulated Depreciation, Machinery	4,200.00	
		Cash (or Accounts Payable)		4,200.00
2.	Dec. 31	Depreciation Expense, Machinery	2,200.00	
		Accumulated Depreciation, Machinery		2,200.00

Part VII

1.	Jan. 5	Machinery	7,500.00	
		Cash (or Accounts Payable)		7,500.00
2.	Dec. 31	Depreciation Expense, Machinery	3,750.00	
		Accumulated Depreciation, Machinery		3,750.00

12

Current and Long-Term Liabilities

Your objectives in studying this chapter should include learning how to:

Explain the difference between current and long-term liabilities.

Explain the meaning of definite and estimated liabilities.

Record transactions involving liabilities such as property taxes payable, product warranties, and short-term notes payable.

Calculate the present value of a sum of money to be received a number of periods in the future or to be received periodically.

Account for long-term noninterest-bearing notes payable and for capital and operating leases.

Define or explain the words and phrases listed in the chapter Glossary.

Topical Outline

I. Definition and classification

    A. Liabilities—obligations resulting from past transactions that require the future payment of assets or the future performance of services.

    B. Current liabilities—debts or other obligations, the liquidation of which is expected to require the use of existing current assets or the creation of other current liabilities.

    C. Long-term liabilities—obligations that will not require the use of existing current assets because they do not mature within one year or one operating cycle.

    D. Definite liabilities—liabilities may be indefinite with respect to:

        1. Identity of the creditor.
        2. Due date of the debt.
        3. Amount to be paid (in which case the liability is called an estimated liability).

    E. Estimated liabilities—obligations that definitely exist but for which the amounts to be paid are uncertain.

        1. Property taxes payable.
        2. Product warranty liabilities.

    F. Contingent liabilities—are not existing obligations and are not recorded as liabilities.

        1. Potential legal claims.
        2. Debt guaranties.

II. Short-term notes payable

    A. Examples

        1. Note given to secure a time extension on an account—provides a written promise to pay and specifies a rate of interest that will apply to the debt.
        2. Note given to secure borrowing from a bank

            a. Loan—cash proceeds equal to the face value of the note; the note is a promise to repay the face value of the note plus interest.
            b. Discount—cash proceeds equal to the face value of the note less interest that is deducted in advance; the note is a promise to repay the face value of the note.

    B. End-of-period adjustments

        1. Accrued interest expense on outstanding notes payable should be recorded at the end of the accounting period.
        2. Interest on a discounted note must be allocated to the periods benefited.

III. Present value

    A. The concept: a dollar received in the future is worth less than a dollar received today because the dollar received today can be invested to earn more than a dollar in the future.

    B. Present value tables—used to solve present value problems instead of a formula.

        1. "Present value of $1" table used for problem based on single payments.
        2. "Present value of $1 received periodically for a number of periods" used for problem based on a number of equal payments.
        3. Interest rates normally expressed in annual amounts.
        4. Discount periods can be any length of time; if less than a year, annual interest rate must be adjusted for the discount period.

IV. Exchanging a note for a plant asset

    A. Two elements may or may not be stipulated in the note:

1. A dollar amount equivalent to the bargained cash price of the asset.
2. An interest factor to compensate the supplier for the use of the funds that otherwise would have been received in a cash sale.

B. Asset should be recorded at its cash price or at the present value of the note, whichever is more clearly determinable.
C. A Discount on Notes Payable is created if the note does not have a stated interest rate or if the interest rate is unreasonably low. The discount is amortized over the life of the note.

V. Liabilities from leasing

A. Capital lease (or financing lease)—must meet any one of four criteria:

1. Ownership of the leased asset is transferred to the lessee at the end of the lease period.
2. The lease gives the lessee the option of purchasing the leased asset at less than fair value at some point during or at the end of the lease period.
3. The period of the lease is 75 percent or more of the estimated service life of the leased asset.
4. The present value of the minimum lease payments is 90 percent or more of the fair value of the leased asset.

B. Operating lease—any lease that does not meet any one of the preceding criteria.
C. Accounting for leases

1. Capital lease—treated as a purchase transaction. The present value of the lease payments constitutes the cost of the asset and is debited to an asset account.
2. Operating lease—annual rental payments for leased asset, as well as payments for taxes, insurance and repairs, are charged to expense.

Part I

Many of the important ideas and concepts discussed in Chapter 12 are reflected in the following list of key terms. Test your understanding of these terms by matching the appropriate definitions with the terms. Record the number identifying the most appropriate definition in the blank space next to each term.

_____	Bank discount	_____	Financing lease
_____	Capital lease	_____	Long-term liabilities
_____	Carrying amount of a note	_____	Operating lease
_____	Carrying amount of a lease	_____	Present value
_____	Estimated liability	_____	Present value table
		_____	Product warranty

1. A lease not meeting any one of the criteria of the FASB that would make it a capital lease.

2. The remaining lease liability minus the unamortized discount on the lease financing.

3. Interest charged and deducted by a bank at the time a loan is made.

4. An obligation that definitely exists but for which the amount to be paid is uncertain.

5. A table showing the present values of one amount to be received at various future dates when discounted at various interest rates.

6. A lease having essentially the same economic consequences as if the lessee had secured a loan and purchased the leased asset.

7. A promise to a customer that obligates the seller or manufacturer for a limited period of time to pay for items such as replacement parts or repair costs if the product breaks or fails to perform.

8. Another name for a capital lease.

9. Debts or obligations that will not require the use of existing assets in their liquidation because they do not mature within one year or one operating cycle, whichever is longer.

10. The face amount of a note minus the unamortized discount on the note.

11. The estimated worth today of an amount of money to be received at a future date.

Part II

Complete the following by filling in the blanks.

1. Use the present value tables in the text to calculate the following present values:

   a. $1 to be received 12 years hence at 10%. $ _____

   b. $2,000 to be received 14 years hence, at 8%. $ _____

   c. $1 to be received at the end of each year for 20 years, at 14%.

      $ _____

   d. $1,000 to be received at the end of each period for 10 periods at 16%.

      $ _____

2. Two important examples of estimated liabilities are (a) _____ _____, and (b) _____ _____.

3. If a company discounts its $2,000 note payable at the bank, the cash proceeds of the note which the company receives is (less than, equal to, more than) _____ _____ $2,000.

4. When the rate of interest on an investment is 9% compounded annually, the present value of $1,000 to be received three years hence is the amount of money that must be invested today that together with the 9% compound interest earned on the investment will equal $ _____ at the end of three years. The amount is $1,000 × _____ = _____.

5. When the account Discount on Notes Payable is shown on the balance sheet, does it increase or decrease the carrying amount of Notes Payable? _____

6. Certain leases have essentially the same economic consequences as if the lessee secured a loan and purchased the leased asset. These leases are known as _____ _____.

7. If the interest rate is changed from 5 percent to 8 percent, will the present value of $1 to be received in one year be increased or decreased? _____

8. Long-term liabilities are obligations that will not require the use of _____ _____ in their liquidation.

160

Part III

A company prepares monthly financial statements and estimates property taxes based on last year's tax rate. The assessed valuation of property owned by the company is $120,000. Last year's tax levy was $0.80 per $100.

(a) Present a general journal entry to record the property tax for January.

DATE	ACCOUNT TITLES AND EXPLANATION	P.R.	DEBIT	CREDIT

(b) In August the current year's levy is determined to be $1.00. Present the general journal entry to pay the annual tax at the end of August and to record the expense for August.

DATE	ACCOUNT TITLES AND EXPLANATION	P.R.	DEBIT	CREDIT

Part IV

Glitz Company estimates that future costs to satisfy its product warranty obligation amount to 3% of sales. In January, the company sold merchandise for $50,000 cash and paid $1,200 to repair products returned for warranty work. Present general journal entries to record these transactions.

DATE	ACCOUNT TITLES AND EXPLANATION	P.R.	DEBIT	CREDIT

Part V

A company whose accounting periods end each December 31 discounted its own $10,000, noninterest-bearing note at its bank for 60 days at 12% on December 16, 198A. Complete the following entries involving this note.

DATE		ACCOUNT TITLES AND EXPLANATION	P.R.	DEBIT	CREDIT
198A					
Dec.	16				
		Discounted our noninterest-bearing note for 60 days			
		at 10%.			
	31				
		To set up as a contra liability the interest applicable			
		to 198A.			
198B					
Jan.	1				
		To reverse the adjusting entry that set out the			
		discount on our note payable.			
Feb.	14				
		Paid our discounted note payable.			

Part VI

Assume that on January 2, 198A, a day on which the prevailing interest rate was 12%, a company exchanged a $15,000, five-year, noninterest-bearing note payable for a machine, the cash price of which was not readily determinable.

1. The present value of the note on the day of exchange and the amount at which the machine should be recorded is calculated:

   $15,000 × _____ = $ _____.

2. The entry to record the exchange is:

DATE	ACCOUNT TITLES AND EXPLANATION	P.R.	DEBIT	CREDIT

3. The amount of discount to be amortized at the end of the first year in the five-year life of the note is calculated:

   $ _____ × 12% = $ _____.

4. The discount amortization entry at the end of the first year is:

DATE	ACCOUNT TITLES AND EXPLANATION	P.R.	DEBIT	CREDIT

5. The note should appear on the company's balance sheet at the end of its first year as follows:

Part VII

On January 1, 198A, Nord Company signed a 10-year lease agreement under which it promises to pay $30,000 per year in return for the use of some equipment. Assume the lease should be classified as a capital lease, and an interest rate of 12% is reasonable.

1. Prepare a general journal entry to record the lease.

DATE	ACCOUNT TITLES AND EXPLANATION	P.R.	DEBIT	CREDIT

2. Prepare a general journal entry to record the first $30,000 lease payment on December 31, 198A.

DATE	ACCOUNT TITLES AND EXPLANATION	P.R.	DEBIT	CREDIT

3. Prepare a general journal entry to record depreciation expense on December 31, 198A. Use straight-line depreciation and no salvage value.

DATE	ACCOUNT TITLES AND EXPLANATION	P.R.	DEBIT	CREDIT

4. Prepare a general journal entry to amortize the discount on lease financing for 198A.

DATE	ACCOUNT TITLES AND EXPLANATION	P.R.	DEBIT	CREDIT

Solutions for Chapter 12

Part I

Part II

1. a. $0.3186
   b. $681
   c. $6.6231
   d. $4,833

2. a. property taxes
   b. product warranties

3. less than

4. $1,000, $1,000 × 0.7722 = $772.20

5. decrease

6. capital leases (or financing leases)

7. decreased

8. existing current assets

Part III

(a)

| Jan. 31 | Property Taxes Expense .... | 80.00 | |
| | Estimated Property Taxes Payable .... | | 80.00 |

[($120,000/$100) × $0.80]/12 = $80

(b)

Aug. 31	Property Taxes Expense	240.00	
	Prepaid Property Taxes (Sept.–Dec.)	400.00	
	Estimated Property Taxes Payable (7 × $80)	560.00	
	Cash		1,200.00

($120,000/$100) × $1.00 = $1,200

($1,200/12) × 4 = $400

Part IV

Jan.	--	Cash	50,000.00	
		Sales		50,000.00
	--	Warranty Expense ($50,000 × .03)	1,500.00	
		Estimated Warranty Liability		1,500.00
	--	Estimated Warranty Liability	1,200.00	
		Cash		1,200.00

Part V

198A				
Dec.	16	Cash	9,800.00	
		Interest Expense	200.00	
		Notes Payable		10,000.00
	31	Discount on Notes Payable	50.00	
		Interest Expense		50.00
198B				
Jan.	1	Interest Expense	50.00	
		Discount on Notes Payable		50.00
Feb.	14	Notes Payable	10,000.00	
		Cash		10,000.00

Part VI

1. $15,000 × 0.5674 = $8,511

2.
Jan.	2	Machinery	8,511.00	
		Discount on Notes Payable	6,489.00	
		Long-Term Notes Payable		15,000.00

3. $8,511 × 12% = $1,021.32

4.
Dec. 31	Interest Expense	1,021.32	
	Discount on Notes Payable		1,021.32

5. Long-term liabilities:

Long-term notes payable	$15,000.00	
Less unamortized discount based on the 12% interest rate prevailing on the date of issue	5,467.68*	$9,532.32

---

*$6,489.00 − $1,021.32 = $5,467.68

Part VII

1. 198A
   Jan. 1 Equipment 169,506.00
          Discount on Lease Financing 130,494.00
             Long-term Lease Liability 300,000.00
             ($30,000 × 5.6502 = $169,506)

2. Dec. 31 Long-term Lease Liability 30,000.00
              Cash 30,000.00

3.   31 Depreciation Expense, Equipment 16,950.60
              Accumulated Depr., Equipment 16,950.60
              ($169,506/10 = $16,950.60)

4.   31 Interest Expense 20,340.72
              Discount on Lease Financing 20,340.72
              ($169,506 × 12% = $20,340.72)

13

Payroll Accounting

Your objectives in studying this chapter should include learning how to:

List the taxes that are withheld from employees' wages and the payroll taxes that are levied on employers.

Calculate an employee's gross pay and the various deductions from the pay.

Prepare a Payroll Register and make the entries to record its information and to pay the employees.

Explain the operation of a payroll bank account.

Calculate and prepare the entries to record the payroll taxes levied on an employer and to record employee fringe benefit costs.

Define or explain the words and phrases listed in the chapter Glossary.

Topical Outline

I. Payroll accounting—recording liabilities and cash payments to employees—also includes:

    A. Amounts withheld from employees' wages.
    B. Payroll taxes levied on the employer.
    C. Employee (fringe) benefits paid by the employer.

II. The federal Social Security Act provides for a number of programs.

    A. A federal old-age and survivors' benefits program provides retirement benefits based on contributions to the program.

        1. Funds for payment of benefits under the Social Security Act come from payroll taxes.
        2. Payroll taxes (called FICA taxes or social security taxes) are imposed under the Federal Insurance Contributions Act on covered employers and their employees.

    B. Joint federal-state unemployment insurance program

        1. The Federal Unemployment Tax Act levies a tax on employers to cover administrative costs relating to the unemployment insurance program.
        2. State unemployment insurance programs generally levy a tax on employers that is designed to pay unemployment compensation, to encourage the stabilization of employment, and to maintain employment offices.

III. Withholdings from employees' paychecks

    A. Federal income taxes.
    B. City and state income taxes.
    C. Union dues.
    D. Other deductions (such as insurance premiums).

IV. Maintaining payroll records

    A. Timekeeping—compiling a record of time worked by each employee.
    B. Payroll register—summarizes and stores payroll information, such as time worked and applicable rates of pay by employee for each pay period.
    C. Payroll is recorded each pay period with a general journal entry.
    D. Payments to employees

        1. Made from a regular checking account, or
        2. Made through a separate payroll checking account.

    E. Individual earnings record—accumulates earnings and withholdings information for a whole year.
    F. Computerized payroll systems—commonly used by many companies to process their payrolls.

V. Payroll taxes levied on employers

    A. Employer's contribution to the social security retirement program.
    B. Federal unemployment taxes.
    C. State unemployment taxes.

VI. Employee fringe benefit costs

    A. Health insurance, life insurance, disability insurance.
    B. Retirement income plan.
    C. Vacation pay.

Part I

Many of the important ideas and concepts discussed in Chapter 13 are reflected in the following list of key terms. Test your understanding of these terms by matching the appropriate definitions with the terms. Record the number identifying the most appropriate definition in the blank space next to each term.

_____ Clock card

_____ Employee's Individual Earnings Record

_____ Federal depository bank

_____ Federal unemployment tax

_____ FICA taxes

_____ Gross pay

_____ Merit rating

_____ Net pay

_____ Payroll bank account

_____ Payroll tax

_____ State unemployment tax

_____ Timekeeping

_____ Wage bracket withholding table

_____ Withholding allowance

1. A table showing the amounts of income tax to be withheld from employees' wages at various levels of earnings.

2. A tax levied on the amount of a payroll or on the amount of an employee's gross pay.

3. Gross pay minus deductions; in other words, the portion of an employee's earnings that is paid to the employee.

4. A tax levied by the federal government and used to pay a portion of the costs of the joint federal-state unemployment programs.

5. The amount an employee earns before any deductions such as FICA taxes and income tax withholdings.

6. A special bank account into which at the end of each pay period the total amount of an employer's payroll is deposited and on which the employee's payroll checks are drawn.

7. A bank authorized to receive as deposits amounts of money payable to the federal government.

8. A record of an employee's hours worked, gross pay, deductions, net pay, and certain personal information about the employee.

9. Making a record of the time each employee is at his or her place of work.

10. A card used by an employee to record his or her time of arrival and departure to and from work.

11. A rating granted to an employer by a state, which is based on whether or not the employer's employees have experienced periods of unemployment. A good rating reduces the employer's unemployment tax rate.

12. An amount of an employee's annual earnings not subject to income tax; also called a personal exemption.

13. Federal Insurance Contributions Act taxes, otherwise known as social security taxes.

14. A tax levied by a state, the proceeds of which are used to pay benefits to unemployed workers.

Part II

Complete the following by filling in the blanks.

1. A state unemployment merit rating gives employers a reduction in their state unemployment tax rate as an inducement for them to _____
   _____.

2. An employee covered by the Fair Labor Standards Act who works 43 hours in one week must be paid his regular rate of pay for the 43 hours plus overtime premium pay at one half his regular rate for _____ of the 43 hours.

3. All state unemployment insurance programs have three common objectives. These objectives are:

   (a) _____,

   (b) _____,

   and (c) _____.

4. Funds for the payment of federal old-age and survivors' benefits, so-called social security benefits, are raised by payroll taxes imposed under a law called the _____
   _____
   _____.

5. Funds from state unemployment taxes are used to pay _____
   _____.

6. Funds from federal unemployment taxes are used to pay _____
   _____.

7. The amount to be withheld from an employee's wages for federal income taxes is determined by (a) _____
   and (b) _____.

8. Covered employers must pay both federal unemployment taxes and state unemployment taxes under the joint federal-state unemployment insurance program in effect in all states.
   Their employees _____ (do, do not) pay federal unemployment taxes and in most states _____ (are, are not) required to pay state unemployment taxes.

9. According to the wage bracket withholding table of Illustration 13-3 in your text, $ _____ should be withheld from the wages of an employee for federal income taxes if the employee has two exemptions and earned $500 in a week.

10. The Federal Insurance Contributions Act levies a payroll tax on both covered employers and their employees. In 1985 an employer was required to withhold FICA taxes from the wages of employees at the rate of _____ % of each employee's gross earnings, the withholding to continue each year until the tax exempt point is reached. In addition to the employee's FICA tax withholdings, an employer must also pay a FICA tax equal to the sum of the _____ withheld from the wages of all of its employees.

173

Part III

The Payroll Register of Whiteman Sales for the first week of the year follows. The deductions and net pay of the first three employees have been calculated and entered.

1. Use an assumed 7% FICA tax rate and complete the payroll information opposite the name of the last employee, Fred Clarke. In addition to FICA taxes, Mr. Clarke should have $111 of federal income taxes, $20 of medical insurance, and no union dues withheld from his wages, which are chargeable to office salaries.

PAYROLL REGISTER

| EMPLOYEE'S NAME | CLOCK CARD NUMBER | DAILY TIME | | | | | | | TOTAL HOURS | O.T. HOURS | REG. PAY RATE | | EARNINGS | | | | | |
		M	T	W	T	F	S	S					REGULAR PAY		O.T. PREMIUM PAY	GROSS PAY		
Delbert Landau	12	8	8	8	7	4	0	0	35		11	00	385	00		315	00	1
Maria Garza	9	8	8	8	5	4	0	0	33		12	00	396	00		330	00	2
Ralph Webster	15	8	8	7	8	4	0	0	35		13	00	455	00		385	00	3
Fred Clarke	4	8	8	8	8	8	4	0	44	4	14	00						4
																		5

Week ending January 8, 19—

| | DEDUCTIONS | | | | | | | | | | PAYMENT | | | | DISTRIBUTION | | | | | |
	FICA TAXES		FEDERAL INCOME TAXES		HOSPITAL INSUR-ANCE		UNION DUES		TOTAL DEDUC-TIONS		NET PAY		CHECK NUMBER	SALES SALARIES		OFFICE SALARIES		DELIVERY SALARIES	
1	26	95	65	00	20	00	10	00	121	95	263	05						385	00
2	27	72	63	00	20	00	10	00	120	72	275	28		396	00				
3	31	85	68	00	20	00	10	00	129	85	325	15		455	00				
4																			
5																			

174

2. Complete the Payroll Register by totaling its columns, and give the general journal entry to record its information.

DATE	ACCOUNT TITLES AND EXPLANATION	P.R.	DEBIT	CREDIT

Whiteman Sales uses a special payroll bank account in paying its employees. Each payday, after the general journal entry recording the information of its Payroll Register is posted, a single check for the total of the employees' net pay is drawn and deposited in the payroll bank account. This transfers funds equal to the payroll total from the regular bank account to the payroll bank account. Then special payroll checks are written on the payroll bank account and given to the employees. For the January 8 payroll, Check No. 845 was used to transfer funds equal to the total of the employees' net pay from the regular bank account. After this, four payroll checks beginning with payroll Check No.102 were drawn and delivered to the employees.

3. Make the entry to record Check No. 845 in the Check Register below.

4. Enter the payroll check numbers in the Payroll Register.

CHECK REGISTER

DATE	CH. NO.	PAYEE	ACCOUNT DEBITED	P.R.	ACCRUED PAYROLL PAYABLE DR.	CASH CR.

5. In the space below give the general journal entry to record the payroll taxes levied on Whiteman Sales as a result of the payroll entered in its January 8 Payroll Register. The company has a merit rating that reduces its state unemployment tax rate to 1% of the first $7,000 paid each employee. (The federal unemployment tax rate is 0.8%.)

DATE	ACCOUNT TITLES AND EXPLANATION	P.R.	DEBIT	CREDIT

6. On the next page is the individual earnings record of Fred Clarke. Transfer from the Payroll Register on page 174 to Mr. Clarke's earnings record the payroll data for the first pay period of the year.

EMPLOYEE'S INDIVIDUAL EARNINGS RECORD

EMPLOYEE'S NAME Fred Clarke

S.S. ACCT. NO. 119-05-1879   EMPLOYEE NO. 4

HOME
ADDRESS 2590 Columbia Street

NOTIFY IN CASE
OF EMERGENCY Mary Clarke

PHONE
NUMBER 965-5698

EMPLOYED 9/1/80

DATE OF
TERMINATION _____ REASON _____

DATE OF
BIRTH May 20, 1943

DATE
BECOMES 65 May 20, 2008

MALE (x) MARRIED (x) NUMBER OF
FEMALE ( ) SINGLE ( ) EXEMPTIONS 4

PAY
RATE $14.00

OCCUPATION Manager

PLACE Store and office

DATE		TIME LOST		TIME WK.			REG. PAY	O.T. PREM. PAY	GROSS PAY	F.I.C.A. TAXES	FED. INC. TAXES	HOSPI-TAL INSUR-ANCE	UNION DUES	TOTAL DEDUC-TIONS	NET PAY	CHECK NUMBER	CUMU-LATIVE PAY
PER. ENDS	PAID	HRS.	REASON	TOTAL	O.T. HOURS												

Solutions for Chapter 13

Part I

Part II

1. keep their employees employed
2. three
3. (a) to pay unemployment benefits, (b) to encourage the stabilization of employment by covered employers, and (c) to establish and operate employment facilities.
4. Federal Insurance Contributions Act
5. benefits to unemployed workers
6. administrative costs of the joint federal-state unemployment insurance program
7. (a) the amount of his or her wages, (b) the number of his or her exemptions.
8. do not, are not
9. $87
10. 7.05%, FICA taxes

Part III

1., 2., and 4.

EMPLOYEE'S NAME	CLOCK CARD NUMBER	M	T	W	T	F	S	S	TOTAL HOURS	O.T. HOURS	REG. PAY RATE		REGULAR PAY		O.T. PREMIUM PAY		GROSS PAY		
Delbert Landau	12	8	8	8	7	4	0	0	35		11	00	385	00			385	00	1
Maria Garza	9	8	8	8	5	4	0	0	33		12	00	396	00			396	00	2
Ralph Webster	15	8	8	7	8	4	0	0	35		13	00	455	00			455	00	3
Fred Clarke	4	8	8	8	8	8	4	0	44	4	14	00	616	00	28	00	644	00	4
													1,852	00	28	00	1,880	00	5

Week ending January 8, 19—

	FICA TAXES		FEDERAL INCOME TAXES		HOSPITAL INSURANCE		UNION DUES		TOTAL DEDUCTIONS		NET PAY		CHECK NUMBER	SALES SALARIES		OFFICE SALARIES		DELIVERY SALARIES	
1	26	95	65	00	20	00	10	00	121	95	263	05	102					385	00
2	27	72	63	00	20	00	10	00	120	72	275	28	103	396	00				
3	31	85	68	00	20	00	10	00	129	85	325	15	104	455	00				
4	45	08	111	00	20	00			176	08	467	92	105			644	00		
5	131	60	307	00	80	00	30	00	548	60	1,331	40		851	00	644	00	385	00

Jan. 8 Sales Salaries Expense 851.00
Office Salaries Expense 644.00
Delivery Salaries Expense 385.00
    FICA Taxes Payable 131.60
    Employees' Federal Income Taxes Payable 307.00
    Employees' Hospital Insurance Payable 80.00
    Employees' Union Dues Payable 30.00
    Accrued Payroll Payable 1,331.40

3.

CHECK REGISTER

DATE		CH. NO.	PAYEE	ACCOUNT DEBITED	P.R.	ACCRUED PAYROLL PAYABLE DR.					CASH CR.				
Jan.	8	845	Payroll Bank	Accrued Payroll											
			Account	Payable		1	3	3	1	40	1	3	3	1	40

5. Jan. 8 Payroll Taxes Expense 165.44
    FICA Taxes Payable 131.60
    State Unemployment Taxes Payable 18.80
    Federal Unemployment Taxes Payable 15.04

EMPLOYEE'S INDIVIDUAL EARNINGS RECORD

EMPLOYEE'S NAME Fred Clarke

S.S. ACCT. NO. 119-05-1879   EMPLOYEE NO. 4

HOME
ADDRESS 2590 Columbia Street

NOTIFY IN CASE
OF EMERGENCY Mary Clarke

PHONE
NUMBER 965-5698

EMPLOYED 9/1/80

DATE OF
TERMINATION

REASON

DATE OF
BIRTH May 20, 1943

DATE
BECOMES 65 May 20, 2008

MALE ( ) MARRIED (x) NUMBER OF
FEMALE ( ) SINGLE ( ) EXEMPTIONS 4

PAY
RATE $14.00

OCCUPATION Manager

PLACE Store and office

DATE		TIME LOST		TIME WK.													
PER. ENDS	PAID	HRS.	REASON	TOTAL	O.T. HOURS	REG. PAY	O.T. PREM. PAY	GROSS PAY	F.I.C.A. TAXES	FED. INC. TAXES	HOSPI-TAL INSUR-ANCE	UNION DUES	TOTAL DEDUC-TIONS	NET PAY	CHECK NUMBER	CUMU-LATIVE PAY
1/8	1/8			44	4	616 00	28 00	644 00	45 08	111 00	20 00		176 08	467 92	105	644 00

6.

14

Partnership
Accounting

Your objectives in studying this chapter should include learning how to:

List the characteristics of a partnership and explain the importance of mutual agency and unlimited liability to a person about to become a partner.

Allocate partnership earnings to partners (a) on a stated fractional basis, (b) in the partners' capital ratio, and (c) through the use of salary and interest allowances.

Prepare entries for (a) the sale of a partnership interest (b) the admission of a new partner by investment, and (c) the retirement of a partner by the withdrawal of partnership assets.

Prepare entries required in the liquidation of a partnership.

Define or explain the words and phrases listed in the chapter Glossary.

Topical Outline

I. Characteristics of a partnership

    A. A voluntary association.

    B. Based on a contract, which should be in writing but may be only orally expressed.

    C. Limited life—death, bankruptcy, or expiration of the contract period automatically end a partnership.

    D. Mutual agency—every partner is an agent of the partnership and can enter into and bind it to any contract within the normal scope of its business.

    E. Unlimited liability—each partner is responsible for payment of all the debts of the partnership if the other partners are unable to pay a share.

II. Limited partnerships

    A. Two classes of partners

        1. General partner(s)—assumes unlimited liability for the debts of the partnership.

        2. Limited partners—have no personal liability beyond their invested amounts.

    B. "General partnership" often used for partnerships in which all the partners have unlimited liability.

III. Partnership accounting

    A. Owners' equity accounts

        1. Capital account for each partner

        2. Withdrawals account for each partner

    B. Measurement and division of earnings

        1. Partners have no legal right to salary, so there is no salary expense for partners.

        2. In the absence of an agreement, partnership earnings and losses are shared equally among the partners.

        3. Methods of sharing partnership earnings:

            a. On a fractional basis.

            b. Based on the ratio of capital investments.

            c. Based on salary and interest allowances with the remainder in a fixed ratio.

        4. Partners can agree to salary and interest *allowances* when distributing profits to reward unequal contribution of services or capital.

IV. Addition or withdrawal of a partner

    A. Sale of a partnership interest requires that the old partner's capital account be transferred to the new partner's capital account.

    B. Investing in an existing partnership

        1. Partnership assets are increased.

        2. The agreement may involve a bonus to the old partners or to the new partner.

        3. A bonus involves a transfer of capital account balances between the partners.

    C. Withdrawal of a partner depends on the partnership agreement.

        1. Partnership assets may be revalued.

        2. The agreement may result in a partner taking assets of greater or lesser value than his or her book equity.

        3. The capital accounts of the partners may require adjustment to reflect the agreed-upon division of assets when a partner withdraws.

V. Liquidations of partnerships

    A. As assets are sold, gains or losses must be recorded.

    B. Partnership creditors must be paid before partners.

C. If a partner's capital account is not sufficient to absorb his or her share of liquidation losses:

1. He or she must, if possible, contribute assets to the partnership to cover the deficiency.
2. Otherwise, the remaining partners' capital accounts must be charged for the capital deficiency of the defaulting partner.

Part I

Many of the important ideas and concepts discussed in Chapter 14 are reflected in the following list of key terms. Test your understanding of these terms by matching the appropriate definitions with the terms. Record the number identifying the most appropriate definition in the blank space next to each term.

_____ Deficit   _____ Liquidation

_____ General partner   _____ Mutual agency

_____ General partnership   _____ Partnership

_____ Limited partners   _____ Partnership contract

_____ Limited partnership   _____ Unlimited liability of partners

1. The legal characteristic of a partnership whereby each partner is an agent of the partnership and is able to bind the partnership to contracts within the normal scope of the partnership business.

2. The document setting forth the agreed terms under which the members of a partnership will conduct the partnership business.

3. A negative balance in an account.

4. The winding up of a business by converting its assets to cash and distributing the cash to the proper parties.

5. A partner who assumes unlimited liability for the debts of the partnership.

6. A partnership that has two classes of partners, limited partners and one or more general partners.

7. The legal characteristic of a partnership that makes each partner responsible for paying all the debts of the partnership if his or her partners are unable to pay their shares.

8. A partnership in which all partners have unlimited liability for partnership debts.

9. Partners who have no personal liability for debts of the limited partnership beyond the amounts they have invested in the partnership.

10. An association of two or more persons to carry on a business as co-owners for profit.

Part II

Complete the following by filling in the blanks.

1. Partnership account is exactly like that of a single proprietorship except for transactions affecting _____.

2. Four advantages of a partnership over the single proprietorship and corporation forms of organization are:

    (a) _____

    _____;

    (b) _____

    _____;

    (c) _____

    _____;

    (d) _____

    _____.

3. A _____ (limited, general) partnership has two classes of partners.

4. Although a partner does not work for either a salary or interest, to be fair in the distribution of partnership earnings, it is often necessary to recognize that the earnings do include a return

    for _____ and a return on _____.

5. Blake and Dillon are partners who have always shared incomes and losses equally. Hester has sued the partners on a partnership debt and obtained a $12,000 judgment. The partnership and Dillon have no assets; consequently, Hester is attempting to collect the entire $12,000 from Blake. Blake has sufficient assets to pay the judgment but refuses, claiming she

    is liable for only one half the $12,000. Hester _____ (can, cannot)

    collect the entire $12,000 from Blake because _____

    _____.

6. Since a partnership is a voluntary association, an individual _____ (can, cannot) be forced against his will to become a partner; and since a partnership is based on a

    contract, its life is _____.

7. The fact that partners cannot enter into an employer-employee contractual relation with themselves supports the contention held in law and custom that partners work for partnership

    _____ and not for a salary. Fur-

    thermore, partners invest in a partnership for _____ and not for interest.

8. The phrase mutual agency when applied to a partnership means _____

    _____

    _____.

9. Jay and Faye are partners in the operation of an insurance agency. Business has been slow, and without consulting Faye, Jay entered into a contract with Rays Limited to purchase three satellite dishes to be sold by the partnership. Faye repudiated the contract. If Rays Limited attempts to hold the partnership liable on the contract, it _____ (can, cannot) do so because _____
_____.

Part III

Flip and Flop began a partnership by investing $14,000 and $10,000, respectively, and during its first year the partnership earned a $21,000 net income. *Required:* Complete the tabulation below to show under the several assumptions the share of each partner in the $21,000 net income.

	Flip's Share	Flop's Share
1. The partners failed to agree as to the method of sharing	$	$
2. The partners had agreed to share in their beginning-of-year investment ratio	$	$
3. The partners had agreed to share by giving a $8,200 per year salary allowance to Flip and a $9,000 per year salary allowance to Flop, plus 10% interest on their beginning-of-year investments, and the remainder equally	$	$

Part IV

1. Assume that the partnership of Flip and Flop (Part III above) earned $14,000 rather than $21,000 and that the partners had agreed to share incomes and losses by giving salary allowances of $8,200 and $9,000 respectively, 10% interest on beginning investments, and the remainder equally. Flip's share of the $14,000 would be $ _____, and Flop's share would be $ _____.

2. Also, if Flip and Flop share incomes and losses as immediately above, and the partnership incurred a $3,800 loss rather than a profit, Flip's share of the loss would be $ _____ and Flop's share would be $ _____.

Part V

Use the following balance sheet information to complete the work below.

PINTER, KING AND TODD
Balance Sheet
December 31, 19—

Assets		Owners' Equities	
Cash	$ 8,000	Martin Pinter, capital	$ 9,000
Other assets	$19,000	Mike King, capital	$ 9,000
		Harold Todd, capital	$ 9,000
Total assets	$27,000	Total owners' equities	$27,000

1. Martin Pinter has a $9,000 equity in the partnership of Pinter, King and Todd. If with the consent of his partners, he sells his equity to Lee Russell for $9,000, the entry to record the transaction is:

DATE	ACCOUNT TITLES AND EXPLANATION	P.R.	DEBIT	CREDIT

2. If rather than selling the equity for $9,000, Pinter sold it for $10,000, the entry _____ (would, would not) be the same.

Part VI

The condensed balance sheet of Shaw, Greene, and Wilson, who have always shared incomes and losses in a 3:2:1 ratio follows. Wilson plans to leave the partnership. Shaw and Greene plan to continue the business under a new partnership contract.

SHAW, GREENE, AND WILSON
Balance Sheet
December.31, 19—

Assets		Owners' Equities	
Cash	$10,000	Edmund Shaw, capital	$17,000
Other assets	30,000	Bernard Greene, capital	15,000
		Graham Wilson, capital	8,000
Total assets	$40,000	Total owners' equities	$40,000

1. If Wilson takes $8,000 of partnership cash in settlement for his equity, the remaining assets will total $ _____; Shaw's equity in the remaining assets will be $ _____; and Greene's equity will be $ _____.

2. If Wilson takes $9,000 of partnership cash in settlement for his equity, the remaining assets will be $ _____; Shaw's equity in the remaining assets will be $ _____; and Greene's equity will be $ _____.

3. If Wilson takes $7,500 of partnership cash in settlement for his equity, the remaining assets will total $ _____; Shaw's equity in these assets will be $ _____; and Greene's equity will be $ _____.

Part VII

Wheeler, Carson, and Young, who have operated a partnership for a number of years, sharing incomes and losses equally, are to liquidate. The assets and equities of the partnership just prior to its liquidation are shown in the T-accounts below.

Cash			Accounts Payable		
Dec. 31	9,000			Dec. 31	9,000

Other Assets			Wheeler, Capital		
Dec. 31	29,000			Dec. 31	12,000

Loss or Gain from Realization			Carson, Capital		
				Dec. 31	9,000

			Young, Capital		
				Dec. 31	8,000

1. Make entries directly in the T-accounts to record the sale of the other assets under the assumption that the other assets are sold for $20,000.

2. Make entries directly in the T-accounts to allocate the loss from realization to the partners.

3. Since the creditor claims take precedence over the claims of the partners, make entries in the T-accounts to pay the creditors.

4. Fill in the blanks in the following statements:

At this point in the liquidation of the partnership of Wheeler, Carson, and Young, after losses are shared and the creditors are paid, the balance of the Cash account is $ _____ and is equal to the sum of the balances of the _____ accounts. The balances of the partners' capital accounts are: Wheeler, $ _____; Carson, $ _____; and Young $ _____. Consequently, in a final distribution of cash Wheeler would receive $ _____, Carson should receive $ _____, and Young should receive $ _____.

Solutions for Chapter 14

Part I

Part II

1. the partners' equities

2. (a) Brings more money and skills together than a single proprietorship
   (b) Is easier to organize than a corporation
   (c) Does not have the corporation's governmental supervision or extra burden taxation
   (d) Allows partners to act freely and without the necessity of stockholders' and directors' meetings, as is required in a corporation

3. limited

4. services, investments

5. can, each partner is unlimitedly liable for the debts of the partnership

6. cannot, limited

7. profits or earnings, profits or earnings

8. each partner is an agent of the partnership and can bind it to contracts

9. cannot, the sale of satellite dishes is not the normal business of an insurance agency

Part III

1. $10,500, $10,500

2. $12,250, $8,750

3. $10,300, $10,700

Part IV

1. $6,800, $7,200

2. ($2,100), ($1,700)

Part V

1. Dec. 31 Martin Pinter, Capital 9,000.00
                     Lee Russell, Capital 9,000.00

2. would be

Part VI

1. $32,000; $17,000; $15,800.
2. $31,000; $16,400; $14,600.
3. $32,500; $17,300; $15,200.

Part VII

1., 2., and 3

Cash			
Dec. 31	9,000	Dec. 31	9,000
31	20,000		

Accounts Payable			
Dec. 31	9,000	Dec. 31	9,000

Other Assets			
Dec. 31	29,000	Dec. 31	29,000

Wheeler, Capital			
Dec. 31	3,000	Dec. 31	12,000

Loss or Gain from Realization			
Dec. 31	9,000	Dec. 31	9,000

Carson, Capital			
Dec. 31	3,000	Dec. 31	9,000

Young, Capital			
Dec. 31	3,000	Dec. 31	8,000

4. Cash, $20,000, partners' capital. Partners' capital account balances: Wheeler, $9,000; Carson, $6,000; Young, $5,000. Wheeler should receive $9,000; Carson should receive $6,000; and Young should receive $5,000.

Notes

Notes

Notes

Notes

Notes

Notes

Notes